Return of the Ether

*When Theory
and Reality Collide*

Sid Deutsch

SciTech
PUBLISHING, INC.
Mendham, NJ

Printed in the United States of America

10   9   8   7   6   5   4   3   2   1

ISBN 1-891121-10-3

SciTech books may be purchased at quantity discounts for educational,
business, or sales promotional use. For information, contact the publisher:

SciTech Publishing, Inc.
89 Dean Road
Mendham, NJ 07945
e-mail: scitech@worldnet.att.net
www.scitechpub.com

Contents

Preface   **v**

Chapter 1   **The Reasons for This Book**   **1**
1-1. Introduction   1
1-2. Quantum Reality   7
1-3. Brief Reviews of Each Chapter   11
1-4. Pros and Cons of Conjecture   13

Chapter 2   **Determinism**   **15**
2-1. Capitulation to "Somehow"   15
2-2. Planetary Motion   19
2-3. Hydrogen Atom's Electron Motion   20
2-4. Radioactive Decay   22

Chapter 3   **The Photon Model**   **29**
3-1. A Sound Wave   29
3-2. Electromagnetic Field   32
3-3. Two-Slit Interference Pattern   35
3-4. Simultaneous-Burst Pattern   39
3-5. Individual-Photon Pattern   40
3-6. The Wave-Particle Duality Field   41
3-7. Interferometer Experiment   48
3-8. Decaying-Exponential WPD Field   53

Chapter 4   **The Electron Model**   **55**
4-1. Relativistic Changes   55
4-2. Two-Slit Interference Pattern   60
4-3. Simultaneous-Burst Pattern   64

4-4. Individual-Electron Pattern   64
4-5. The Particle-Wave Duality Field   66
4-6. Electron-Spin Experiment   70
4-7. Decaying-Exponential PWD Field   72

Chapter 5   The Hydrogen Atom   75
5-1. Some Orbital Peculiarities   75
5-2. Orbital Specifications   76
5-3. Stable Orbits Versus PWD
        Frequencies   78
5-4. Synchrotron Radiation   83

Chapter 6   Bell's Theorem   89
6-1. Twin-State Photon Generator   89
6-2. Calcite Filters   90
6-3. Experiment Using Calcite Filters   95
6-4. Two Conjectures That Can Explain
        the Discrepancy   98
6-5. Experiment Using Interferometers   103

Chapter 7   Special Relativity   109
7-1. Some Principles of Special
        Relativity   109
7-2. The Lorentz Contraction   111
7-3. Time Dilation   115
7-4. Conventional Doppler Shift   117
7-5. Relativistic Doppler Shift   120
7-6. Doppler Shifts of Approaching
        Generators   123

Chapter 8   Model of the Universe   127
8-1. The Big Bang   127
8-2. The First Few Minutes   131
8-3. Formation of Structures   134
8-4. Galactic Recession   135
8-5. The Hubble Constant   138
8-6. Some Galactic Peculiarities   139
8-7. Entropy   141
8-8. A Re-entrant Steady-State Universe   142
8-9. The Ether   145

References   151
Appendix   Equations   153
Index   163
About the Author   169

Preface

There is no sharp dividing line between the academic upbringing of an electrical engineer versus that of a physicist. As an electrical engineer, I always vaguely knew that many physicists had difficulty swallowing some of the unrealistic tenets of quantum mechanics. Out of curiosity, when "semi-retirement" gave me enough time to do so, I decided to read up on "quantum reality."

Here is a list of six representative reading materials in chronological order (see the References to identify the publishers):

M. Gardner, *Quantum Weirdness,* 1982.

N. Herbert, *Quantum Reality,* 1985.

J. Baggott, *The Meaning of Quantum Theory,* 1992.

R. Mills, *Space, Time, and Quanta,* 1994.

D. Lindley, *Where Does the Weirdness Go?,* 1996.

A. Watson, *Quantum Spookiness Wins, Einstein Loses in Photon Test,* 1997.

In addition, there are several books that are so badly written (in my opinion, of course) that I will not advertise them by adding them to the list.

The upshot of all the reading was this: It seemed almost obvious to me that much of quantum weirdness can be explained by an all-pervading ether (or aether, as it is sometimes spelled).

The ether was "invented" by James Clerk Maxwell and his contemporaries, around 1860, to account for the fact that one can transmit an electromagnetic field through a "vacuum." The conjecture was that a vacuum is really filled by this mysterious substance, the ether. The concept was analogous to the way in which a sound wave is transmitted through, say, air.

If air is moving with respect to a loudspeaker, one can easily find the wind velocity by measuring the wavelength of sound as it propagates upstream, downstream, and across stream with respect to the wind. Well, in 1887, Albert A. Michelson and Edward W. Morley tried to find the ether's velocity, with respect to the earth's rotation around the sun, by measuring the wavelength of light as it propagates "upstream, downstream, and across stream." Their data showed that the velocity of the ether is zero, which dealt a serious blow to the ether concept. One possible explanation is that every large object, such as the earth, carries its own ether along as it hurtles through space. After all, this is exactly how the atmosphere is carried along by the earth as it hurtles through space.

Eventually, the "big shots" of physics (as David Bohm called them) chose to abandon the ether. As Edmund T. Whittaker (1951) put it in his preface to *A History of the Theories of Aether and Electricity: The Classical Theories*:

"A word might be said about the title *Aether and Electricity*. As everyone knows, the aether played a great part in the physics of the nineteenth century; but in the first decade of the twentieth, chiefly as a result of the failure of attempts to observe the earth's motion relative to the aether, and the acceptance of the principle that such attempts must always fail, the word 'aether' fell out of favour, and it became customary to refer to the interplanetary spaces as 'vacuous'; the vacuum being conceived as mere emptiness, having no properties except that of propagating electromagnetic waves."

But my resuscitation of the ether is based on the behavior of *single, isolated photons and electrons,* and not on a large object such as the earth. However, restoration of the ether for subatomic particles implies that "every large object, such as the earth, carries its own ether along as it hurtles through space"; in fact, it implies that the universe is filled with ether, as it was in Maxwell's day.

There are so many aspects to this "return of the ether" that I had enough material for a short book. Accordingly, having previously authored or co-authored five technical books, I had a great deal of fun writing an earlier version of the present book. The manuscript was intended for "intelligent laypersons."

Alas, it was not publishable. Although conjectures are always being published (frequently as the scientific "truth"), my manuscript had too many conjectures. Just as we have infinity versus infinity squared, my contribution was like conjectures squared. The publishers said, justifiably, "First get the physics people to accept your thesis."

Next, I extracted short bits and pieces of the manuscript with the aid of that present-day marvel, a word processor. Typical is some of the material of Chaps. 3 and 4, which appeared on the Internet as "Return of the Ether: Conjecture That Can Explain Photon and Electron Two-Slit Interference," 1 April 1998:

http://xxx.lanl.gov/ftp/physics/papers/9803/9803039.pdf

These short manuscripts were sent to various (mostly physics) publications. They were invariably rejected. Never mind the polite reasons given; I knew, from the start, that there were three strikes against me:

1. The "big shots" had buried the ether some 80 years ago. Therefore, the "return of the ether" was simply a PPP—a preposterous, pernicious proposal.

2. The author is an electrical engineer. Many physicists regard engineers as members of a lower caste because engineers "get their hands dirty" by getting things to work. This is analogous to the attitude of the Lord of the Manor, who looks down upon his gardeners. The ether could only be revived by a physicist.

3. Normally, the restoration of the ether is a conjecture that should be presented first as a paper at a physics convention. It should be exposed to the critical scrutiny of physics reviewers. I plead guilty; I could not see myself hanging my laundry in public and defending a preposterous, pernicious proposal. It was much easier to make some minor changes, and dash off to a publisher. As a Visiting Professor, I was not concerned with "publish or perish"; at my advanced age, it would be more appropriate to say "publish *and* perish."

So much for the narrative about how this book came to be written. I received critical comments from several people but, because the book is controversial, I refrain from formally acknowledging them by name.

I am thankful, however to the people of the Electrical Engineering Department of the University of South Florida, in Tampa, for their "southern hospitality"—especially Department Head Dr. Elias Stefanakos, and

Horace Gordon and Tom Smith, and Dr. Michael Kovac, Dean of Engineering. Special thanks are also due to Dudley R. Kay and Denise G. May of SciTech Publishing, Inc.; to my daughter Alice, President of Bioscreen, who made many helpful comments as an "intelligent layperson"; and to my wife, Ruth, who brought into being an environment that was conducive to "creative conjecture."

Sid Deutsch
Sarasota, Florida

Chapter 1

The Reasons for This Book

1-1. Introduction

I remember, many years ago, when my classroom teacher placed a ringing bell under a jar. He (or was it she?) attached a small pump, and proceeded to remove the air from the jar. As the vacuum state approached, the loudness diminished, showing that air in the jar was necessary to conduct the bell's sound to the student audience in the room.

What is a vacuum? The absence of air? Nothing? Repeat the above experiment if a magnet is placed across the jar: It will turn out that removing the air has no effect upon the magnetic field in the jar. Similarly, repeat the experiment if electrodes attached to a battery, are say, placed across the jar: If we test for the electric field, it will turn out that removing the air has negligible effect upon the electric field in the jar.

It would certainly help if we knew what magnetic and electric fields really are, but the fact nevertheless remains: A vacuum is more than "nothing." It can sustain magnetic and electric fields. This much was known by the "ancients"—physicists in 1864. At that time, James Clerk Maxwell (1831–1879) presented the equations that describe an electromagnetic field (EMF). According to Maxwell (with the mathematics omitted), a changing magnetic field generates a changing electric field, which in turn generates a changing magnetic field, and so on and so on.

Maxwell and his contemporaries were of the opinion that so-called empty space, or a vacuum, is really filled with a mysterious substance, "the ether" (or the aether, as it is sometimes spelled). The reasoning behind the ether is this: Sound is transmitted as one molecule pushes (and pulls a neighbor, in effect, by leaving a hole) in the direction of propagation; similarly, an EMF is transmitted as one microvolume of ether pushes (and pulls a neighbor, in effect, by leaving a hole) at right angles to the direction of propagation. The velocity of sound is determined by the density and elasticity of the medium; similarly, the velocity of an EMF is determined by whatever corresponds to the density and elasticity of the ether. (This is further discussed in Chap. 3.)

But with the arrival of the twentieth century, alas, the world of Maxwell and Isaac Newton (1642–1727) has been modified by a considerable degree of scientific complexity. *The ether has been abandoned,* and quantum mechanics has changed the way we look at the atomic and subatomic world.

Quantum mechanics gets its name from the fact that energy is quantized; it is as if you could have a 60- or 61-watt bulb, but anything in between, such as 60.3 W, is impossible. (The electric bill that you get every month is quantized to the nearest penny.) We are acquainted, of course, with the quantization of matter via electrons, protons, neutrons, atoms, and so forth. Less obvious is the fact that the quantization of energy means that electromagnetic waves are quantized. Radio waves, visible light, and X rays all arrive as minuscule electromagnetic wave packets called *photons.* The best we can do is represent a photon as some kind of wiggle, of unknown size, as in Fig. 1-1.

The effective mass of a typical photon is 50,000 times *less* than that of an electron. Except for the feeble light coming from celestial objects, or from attenuated sources in a physics laboratory, we are normally immersed in a huge barrage of photons. But this is familiar territory; much of the present book is about *individual* photons and electrons, at the limits of knowledge insofar as quantum mechanics is concerned.

By definition, a photon always travels at the speed of light (symbol c). Table 1-1 illustrates various frequencies (and corresponding wavelengths), ranging from those of power stations (60 Hz) to gamma rays (3×10^{21} Hz). The wavelength entries are correct only for a vacuum; in any other medium the velocity of propagation is less than c, depending on the medium.

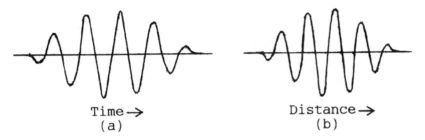

Time →
(a)

Distance →
(b)

Fig. 1-1. The wave packet representation of a photon: (a)The electric (or magnetic) field measured at a particular point in space. The photon flies by at the speed of light, $c = 2.9979 \times 10^8$ meters/second (in a vacuum). The wiggles occur at a frequency f. (b)A "photograph" taken at a particular instant of time. The "size" of a photon is unknown.

Table 1-1. Various electromagnetic frequencies and corresponding wavelengths in vacuum. (Frequency $\times$ wavelength $= c \cong 3 \times 10^8$ m/s.)

Frequency	Wavelength	Application
60 Hz	5000 kilometers	Power stations in United States
3 kHz $= 3 \times 10^3$ Hz	100 kilometers	Approx. low-freq. edge of EMF signaling
1 MHz $= 1 \times 10^6$ Hz	300 meters	Approx. center of AM broadcast band
100 MHz $= 1 \times 10^8$ Hz	3 meters	Approx. center of FM broadcast band
300 GHz $= 3 \times 10^{11}$ Hz	1 millimeter	Approx. low-freq. edge of infrared
4×10^{14} Hz	750 nanometers	Low-freq. edge of visible light
7.9×10^{14} Hz	380 nanometers	High-frequency edge of visible light
3×10^{17} Hz	1 nanometer	Approx. borderline of ultraviolet, X rays
6×10^{18} Hz	0.05 nanometer	Typical X ray
1×10^{20} Hz	3 picometers	Approx. borderline of X rays, gamma rays
3×10^{21} Hz	0.1 picometer	Typical gamma ray

[Some of the numerical values used (or, in some cases, derived) in this book, along with symbols where appropriate, are given in Table 1-2. Most of the values are taken from a small booklet, *Particle Physics* (July 1994), published by the American Institute of Physics. Although the booklet is invaluable, reading it without a magnifying glass can be dangerous to your health.]

It seemed to be eminently reasonable, when Albert Einstein (1879–1955) proposed it as a sort of axiom, that signals cannot travel faster than the speed of light. This was in connection with his special theory of relativity, published

Table 1-2.   Some numerical values.

Name	Symbol	Name	Symbol
Meter	m	Coulomb	C
Second	s	Farad	F
Joule	J	Henry	H
Newton	N	Ohm	Ω
Kilogram	kg	Year	yr
Kelvin°	K	Light-year	lt-yr

Name	Symbol	Numerical value
Speed of light in vacuum	c	2.9979×10^8 m/s
Planck constant	h	6.6261×10^{-34} J·s
Gravitational constant	G	6.6726×10^{-11} N·m²/kg²
Boltzmann constant	k_B	1.38066×10^{-23} J/K
Permittivity of vacuum	ϵ_0	8.8542×10^{-12} F/m
Electrostatic constant	k	8.9876×10^9 N·m²/C²
Permeability of vacuum	μ_0	$4\pi \times 10^{-7}$ H/m
Electron charge	e	1.60218×10^{-19} C
Electron mass	m_0	9.1094×10^{-31} kg
Proton mass		1.67262×10^{-27} kg
Neutron mass		1.67493×10^{-27} kg
Sun's mass	M	1.988×10^{30} kg
Earth's mass		5.974×10^{24} kg
Mean radius of earth's orbit		1.496×10^{11} m
Characteristic imp. of vacuum	Z_0	376.7Ω
Range of strong force		1.4×10^{-15} m
Year	yr	3.1558×10^7 s
Light-year	lt-yr	9.4605×10^{15} m
Parsec		3.262 lt-yr
Hubble constant	H_0	1.847×10^{-18} /s
Age of universe		1.7×10^{10} yr

in 1905. The upper speed limit also applies to gravity waves (gravitons, which have not yet been detected).

But certain questionable "realities" surface from experiments involving *single, individual* electrons and photons. Can we believe that an electron or photon can somehow split in two? Can we believe that photons can somehow influence each other much faster than the speed of light? In the process of answering each of these questions with a loud "**No,**" I came across an almost obvious explanation for the weird experimental results: **Restore the ether!** The "bigshots" [as David Bohm (1919–1992) called them] declared the ether to be dead many years ago. It will be interesting to see if the "youths" who took over will resuscitate the ether.

But perhaps it is a poor pedagogical tactic for me to start with EMFs and quantum theory. They should be viewed against the scientific revolution that began in the 17th century, with Newton. In his "Principia" (1687), Newton gave to the world the mathematical expressions that govern mechanical interactions. These equations happen to be surprisingly simple. Next time you are in an airplane that is accelerating from standstill to takeoff, notice how an invisible force pushes you into the back of the seat. (Whenever that happens, I marvel that those equations learned in school can actually be used to get something off the ground.) Another example is our ability to pinpoint a space satellite to, say, rendezvous with another satellite. (Whenever *that* happens, I marvel at the successful application of Newton's universal law of gravitation.)

In the first example, that of an airplane taking off, the force pushing you into the seat is given by

$$\text{Force } (F) = \text{mass } (m) \times \text{acceleration } (a),$$

where the mass is that of your own body (plus clothes and, perhaps, a laptop word processor).

In the second example, the force of attraction between the satellite and earth is given by

$$\text{Force } (F) = \frac{\text{Gravitational constant } (G) \times \text{mass}_1 (m_1) \times \text{mass}_2 (m_2)}{\text{Distance squared } (d^2)}.$$

This equation requires a bit of explanation. The law is called *universal* because it applies anywhere in the universe—between the earth and the sun, between the moon and earth, between two spherical weights (m_1 and m_2) at a center-to-center distance d apart in a physics laboratory on earth. Precise measurements in the laboratory yield $G = 6.6726 \times 10^{-11}$ newton·meter squared/kilogram squared.

(When I taught physics, I used to assign as a homework problem the calculation of gravitational attraction between two students who were a small but reasonable distance apart. The force turns out to be so small that it is completely ineffective as one of the components of sexual attraction.)

My main point is that our mechanical world rests upon elegant equations such as $F = ma$ and $F = Gm_1m_2/d^2$. Force, mass, acceleration, gravity—all act in accordance with precise numerical relationships.

The unbelievably slow pace of scientific achievement at that time is revealed in that it took some 177 years beyond Newton, in 1864, before Maxwell presented the equations that describe an EMF. Here, again, are two simple equations, but they may be written out in words: First,

A changing magnetic field generates a changing electric field.

In other words, if you wave a magnet in the air, you generate an electric field—a voltage. Normally, nothing comes of this relatively slow hand-waving. In an electric generator, however, the magnets move rapidly across copper conductors; here the voltage results in current that is fed to the generator's load.

Second,

A changing electric field generates a changing magnetic field.

It is not so easy to illustrate this relationship. Magnets are ubiquitous as they hold up promissory notes against refrigerators; but where can we get an electric field? Well, clamp on to the 12-volt terminals of an automobile battery (but don't let the ends of the cable touch, or you may be shocked to see the fireworks that result). If you wave the 12-volt ends in the air, you are generating a minute magnetic field.

But all of this air-waving is crude. A changing magnetic field generates a changing electric field, which in turn.... These are precise cyclic variations that form, loosely speaking, a propagating EMF. At a radio transmitting antenna, the cyclic voltage variation between the ends of the antenna are accompanied by a cyclic magnetic field. The radio signal propagates at the speed of light in a vacuum ($c = 2.9979 \times 10^8$ meters/second, frequently cited as 3×10^8 m/s, also equal to 186,000 miles/second), independent of frequency.

Maxwell's results were a remarkable achievement. They unified electric and magnetic fields, showing that they were related via simple, *precise* mathematical expressions. Taken together with Newton's equations, electrical as well as mechanical phenomena could now be described in uncomplicated terms. Imagine growing up in a world where the laws of the universe were beautifully sparse and unadorned!

This idyllic state sustained a severe blow in 1905 when Einstein reshaped the universe by allowing space to be curved, and time as well as space to be compressed (the Lorentz contraction, discussed in Chap. 7). Further deterioration followed around 1925, when a group of very imaginative physicists, via quantum mechanics, revolutionized our concepts about structure and behavior at atomic levels [A. Hermann, 1971]. Central to this development was Erwin Schrodinger (1887–1961), who in 1926 formulated his famous set of quantum mechanical equations.

Although I frequently refer to "Schrodinger's equations" in the book, it is not necessary for them to be shown here. You can look them up in a book on quantum mechanics; besides, they are more complicated than the Newton or Maxwell equations. But given Schrodinger's equations, one can fully describe the *probabilities* with which an electron, say, will visit a given volume of space. It is necessary to know the boundary conditions, such as the probabilities at the outer confines of the space. The sum of probabilities, taken over all volumes of space, has to be unity.

Maxwell's equations, on the other hand, deal with certainties rather than probabilities. Given Maxwell's equations, we can fully describe the electric and magnetic fields everywhere in space if we are given the boundary conditions, such as the electric and magnetic field intensities at the outer confines of the space.

In the present book, it is not necessary to solve any of these equations. Our individual photons and electrons lead relatively simple lives. Think of Schrodinger's equations as giving the probability that, at a particular point in space, a certain wiggle will show up, say, in the next second. Maxwell's equations tell us that, at this particular point in space, we will measure an electric field of, say, 10 volts/meter.

1-2. Quantum Reality

Three of the most important tenets of quantum mechanics are:

1. Energy is quantized. For an electromagnetic wave, the smallest "chunk" of energy is that of a tiny wave packet, a photon.
2. Quantum mechanics is a method for calculating *probabilities* using Schrodinger's equations. It gives the probabilities (called the

wavefunction) of finding a photon, electron, or whatever, at a particular point in space, given the boundary probability values.
3. There is a wave-particle duality. A wave, such as a photon, also behaves as if it has a certain effective mass. A particle or mass, such as an electron, also behaves as if it is a wave packet (of very high frequency, usually, because an electron is much heavier than a typical photon).

It turns out that much of quantum theory is unbelievable; that is, it runs contrary to common sense. For example, in 1964, John Stewart Bell (1928–1990) "proved" that two photons can influence each other instantaneously, or at least at a velocity far exceeding the speed of light. According to Bell, if the experimenter imparts a change to photon A, it can instantaneously cause a corresponding change to photon B, millions of meters away. This is known as *superluminal* or *nonlocal* signaling (in contrast to conventional communication at or below the speed of light, which is called *local*). As a result of Bell's theorem, and other weird effects (which are considered in subsequent chapters), the subject has been plagued by debate concerning "quantum reality" [H. R. Pagels, 1982; M. Gardner, 1982; P. H. Eberhard and R. R. Ross, 1989; A. Watson, 1997].

I go into the details of Bell's theorem in Chap. 6. For now, it is appropriate to examine the reaction of physicists to the notion of nonlocal communication. At one extreme are those, like myself, who say that "nonlocal" is "non-sense"; that something is missing from Bell's theorem. At the other extreme are those who say that quantum mechanics displays many strange behaviors, and superluminal communication is one of the characteristics that is *somehow* possible.

Consider the following quotations taken from three books that are concerned with quantum reality:

From Nick Herbert, *Quantum Reality,* 1985, page 231:

On the other hand, although Bell's theorem *indirectly* necessitates a deep non-locality, no one has come up with a way to *directly* display this purported non-locality, such as a faster-than-light communication scheme based on these deep quantum connections. If reality research's bottom line is "Reality has consequences," then this Bell-mandated deep reality has so far failed to make a showing. What the future holds for Bell's instantly connected but as yet inaccessible deep reality is anyone's guess.

From Jim Baggott, *The Meaning of Quantum Theory,* 1992, page 138:

This exercise merely confirms once more that quantum theory is not consistent with local reality. Correlations between the photons can be greater than is possible for two Einstein separable particles since the reality of their physical properties is not established until a measurement is made. The two particles are in "communication" over large distances since their behaviour is governed by a common state vector. Quantum theory demands a "spooky action at a distance" that violates special relativity.

From David Lindley, *Where Does the Weirdness Go?*, 1996, page 141:

Bell's theorem, it's important to realize, doesn't involve quantum mechanics at all. It happened that we reached it by thinking of the numerical quantities in it as the results of some quantum mechanical measurements—electron spins or photon polarizations—but that's actually beside the point. The theorem embodies a very general view of reality, one that physicists more or less unthinkingly adhered to before quantum mechanics came along. The fact that Bell's theorem is not obeyed in the real world is telling us not so much that quantum mechanics is correct but that the old view of the world is wrong. But what exactly is that old view, and in what way or ways can it be wrong?

In other words, some 70 years after the principles of quantum mechanics were formulated, many physicists are still debating about whether or not superluminal influences are possible. It seems obvious to me that instantaneous "communication" is *impossible,* and that we must explain, in a sensible manner, why Bell arrived at his conclusions.

I like to think that physics has spawned three Bs that are facetiously reminiscent of music's three Bs. Ours are Niels Bohr (1885–1962), David Bohm, and John S. Bell.

John Horgan recently wrote a book called *The End of Science* (1996), in which he faces "the limits of knowledge in the twilight of the scientific age." I agree with Horgan that, at least where quantum reality is concerned, we are at the "limits of knowledge." The next steps, it seems to me, are "conjectures."

Conjectures are conclusions based on incomplete evidence. For example, the existence of the ether is an unproven conjecture. In the process of conjecturing, however, I repeatedly discovered that it is necessary to resuscitate the ether to get a reasonable explanation of how all of those weird quantum effects come about. The evidence regarding the ether is summarized in the last chapter, Section, 8-9, of this book. Since this is not a mystery novel, I can reveal at the outset that the ether is a perfectly elastic, lossless material. That is, as a photon flies through the ether at a velocity c, each microvolume of ether is set into vibration, propagating the original photonic vibrations without a loss of amplitude. An electron is more complicated because it carries a charge (which is another unknown subatomic attribute) and it moves at a velocity less than c, but here also there is no loss in amplitude. Both photons and electrons do not lose energy in flying through the ether; the ether does not interact with our "everyday" world where energy and mass are concerned. Photons and electrons are intimately involved with the ether, but there is never an exchange of energy or mass.

Furthermore, the ether is a "linear" material; that is, thousands of different signals are simultaneously superimposed everywhere around us, yet they do not interact (which is one of the arguments *against* the existence of an ether). Table 1-1 is a good reminder of the many different frequencies that can be flying by, every which way: A very weak 60-Hz power-station "hum"; a signal from practically every long-wave, broadcast AM, short-wave, television, broadcast FM, and UHF station; infrared from manmade heat sources and the sun; visible light; ultraviolet light; and X rays and gamma rays from the sun and outer space. All are in the form of minuscule *photons*. In a nonlinear medium, new sum and difference frequencies would be generated, but this does not happen in the putative ether. Our eyes see the light waves, undisturbed by the myriad of crisscrossing radio waves.

Recently, vague references to a mysterious ethereal substance that fills all of space have turned up. In a "special report" that appeared as this book went to press, three articles in the January 1999 issue of *Scientific American* (pages 45–69) discuss the latest "Revolution in Cosmology." In an introduction, the editors explain that the universe seems to be expanding at an ever faster rate:

> ... If in fact the growth is accelerating, the universe must be filled with some unknown form of matter or energy whose gravity repels rather than attracts. Hitherto unseen energy is, well, a repulsive thought for physicists. ... In this issue, *Scientific American* presents three sides of the story. First, three observers relate how and why their work on supernovae has caused such commotion. Then a theorist explains why these results attest to an ethereal energy that threads empty space. Finally, a pair of cosmologists offer another interpretation that extends the theory of inflation to times "before" the big bang.

Finally, exactly as it is said that "there is nothing new under the sun" (or in the universe, in this case), it turns out that there is a small group of people that has also restored the ether, but generally for different reasons than I did. Probably the best way to pursue these "restorers" is to start with Steven Rado, who is a physicist. He wrote a book titled *Aethro-Kinematics,* (1995), which is available from him at the address given in the References at the end of this book.

Here is Rado's description of what the book is about, taken from the Web site http://www.westworld.com/~srado/indexX.shtml

> Aethro-Kinematics renders an alternate mechanical solution for the polarization of light. Thus, it reinstates Faraday and Maxwell's gaseous model of the Aether and resumes the original task of exploring all "action at a distance forces" as fluid dynamical behavior of the all-pervading Aether.—In Aethro-Kinematics, Aether is taken as an all-pervading gas at an ultra-microscopic order of magnitude. The constituents of this medium, the "Aethrons," are in constant random motion with perfectly elastic collisions, analogous to the atoms of an ideal gas.—This system obeys the simple laws of the Kinetic Theory of Gases.

1-3. Brief Reviews of Each Chapter

A brief review of each chapter follows.

Chapter 2—Determinism. Determinism is the doctrine that every event is the inevitable consequence of antecedent physical conditions. At a macroscopic level, determinism reigns supreme. All of those precise measurements in the physics and electronics laboratories were done to verify the simple equations of Newton and Maxwell. At an atomic level, however, Schrodinger's equations only give probabilities, and the uncertainty principle of Werner Heisenberg (1901–1976) says that, if one can precisely define where a moving particle is at a particular instant of time, its momentum will be uncertain. Conversely, if one can precisely define its momentum at a particular instant of time, its position will be uncertain. (One can exchange different degrees of uncertainty in position for uncertainty in momentum. Similarly, one can exchange uncertainty about energy level for time uncertainty.) This has led many physicists to declare that the future cannot, in principle, be determined from the past.

The viewpoint espoused in Chap. 2 is that this is merely a reflection of our ignorance. Are we to conclude that a minuscule wave packet can "decide" to accelerate or decelerate of its own free will? This concept strains reality, to say the least.

The hydrogen atom, and radioactive decay, are used as vehicles for the discussion in this chapter.

Chapter 3—The Photon Model. A sensational experiment, the most well-known example that strains quantum reality, is the photon two-slit interference pattern. A photon is presumed to be a minuscule wave packet but, if *single, isolated* photons are aimed at a double slit, the lines that build up on the recording film imply that each photon interferes with itself! It is as if the photon splits into two halves. Furthermore, although the interference pattern consists of parallel lines, the photon terminates on only a single point on the film in accordance with its probability density (its probability of reaching that particular point) as a wave packet. The photon wave packet thus also behaves as a particle. The location of the single point is apparently determined by the previous history of the photon. A highly conjectural model for all of this is presented.

The model is used to explain the peculiar result, which defies our everyday experience, of an interferometer experiment.

Chapter 4—The Electron Model. Here I can paraphrase the above review of Chap. 3. A sensational experiment, another well-known example that strains quantum reality, is the electron two-slit interference pattern. An electron, presumed to be a particle, also behaves as a minuscule wave packet. If *single, isolated* electrons are aimed at a double slit, the lines that build up on the recording film [A. Tonomura et al., 1989] imply that each electron interferes with itself! It is as if the electron split into two halves. Furthermore, although the interference pattern consists of parallel lines, the electron terminates on only a single point on the screen in accordance with its probability density as a *wave packet.* The location of the single point is apparently determined by the previous history of the electron. A highly conjectural model for all of this is presented.

The model is used to explain the peculiar results, which defy our everyday experience, of an electron-spin experiment.

Chapter 5—The Hydrogen Atom. Electron orbits of the hydrogen atom reveal at least two peculiarities that are considered in Chap. 5.

First, the allowable orbital frequencies are determined by integer quantum numbers ($n = 1, 2, 3, \ldots$). This is easily explained, however, by the particle-wave duality (PWD) of an electron which, according to the model, is associated with a certain wave-packet frequency, f_{PWD}. The "stable" orbital frequencies are, simply, harmonics of f_{PWD}. As the electron flies along its orbit, it is associated with standing waves consisting of n cycles of the particle-wave duality field.

Second, an electron that follows a circular orbit should generate a synchrotron electromagnetic field. When an electron is captured by a hydrogen proton, however, it ceases to generate synchrotron radiation. Admittedly far-fetched conjectures are offered as an explanation.

Chapter 6—Bell's Theorem. Two experiments are examined with the aim of explaining how their photons apparently instantaneously influence each other despite a large separation distancewise. One experiment uses calcite filters; the other uses interferometers.

Chapter 7—Special Relativity. There is nothing special about the special relativity chapter except for a look at the ether. The Lorentz contraction, time dilation, and Doppler shifts are reviewed. What is the mechanism of the Lorentz contraction? How can the velocity of light be equal to c as measured by a nonaccelerating observer who is receding from us at a velocity of, say, $0.8c$?

Chapter 8—Model of the Universe. The Big Bang and certain galactic peculiarities are reviewed in Chap. 8. Although the Big Bang hypothesis explains many features of the universe, some unrealistic conclusions remain: Because there is insufficient matter, by far, to "close" the universe, it will continue to expand forever. And time began, at $t = 0$, with the Big Bang; at $t < 0$, there was the Big Crunch.

Here the model of a re-entrant steady-state universe is presented. Instead of a Big Bang, we have a steady-state Small Fizz. Time is indeed infinite, but the universe recycles and repeats itself every 34 billion years.

The chapter ends with a discussion of the ether.

1-4. Pros and Cons of Conjecture

Unfortunately, one must be prepared to pay an appreciable price for an assault on superluminal influences and other questionable "realities."

Many of the proposals are conjectures; that is, there is no scientific basis for the arguments other than they "work," with maximum simplicity and effectiveness. On the other hand, pseudoscientific nonsense such as ectoplasm and paranormal "observations" are out; discussions about these topics are more properly the province of *The Skeptical Inquirer,* which is published by the Committee for the Scientific Investigation of Claims of the Paranormal (CSICOP).

There is a prominent school of philosophy that denounces conjectures. "Let the author beware!" In my opinion, very exciting and vital aspects of scientific work are born out of unproven conjectures. Some of these dreams turn out to be nightmares but, in the meantime, they inspire research in the attempt to prove or disprove their claims. In my opinion, the physicists who accept superluminal speeds as being "somehow" possible have surrendered to an unrealistic and stagnating dead end.

So what is left? Unlike many of the physicists at the time of Maxwell's equations, who thought that the basic laws of the universe had now been revealed, we have learned our lesson, are more cautious, and believe that the surface of subatomic reality has barely been scratched. And through it all, the greatest mystery of all time remains—that of human consciousness. How can a protoplasmic assembly of atoms have an awareness of its own existence? It has become fashionable for books about quantum reality to include a section on consciousness. In my opinion, despite many claims to the contrary, even wild conjecture has not come close to a reasonable explanation for consciousness!

Chapter 2

Determinism

2-1. Capitulation to "Somehow"

We are not yet ready to jump into "the photon model." Too many of us are willing to abandon, without a fight, the analytical ability of the human brain, and to say that unrealistic quantum effects are "somehow" possible. There is nothing to be gained from the later chapters of this book if your philosophical outlook is contaminated by capitulation to "somehow."

There are many examples to illustrate this thesis. Two of my favorites—and I trust that they are sufficient to make the point—are planetary motion and the kinetic theory of heat (or kinetic theory of matter).

In ancient times, life was a succession of miracles (and even today, I am sorry to say, a large proportion of people believe that we are frequently assaulted by unidentified flying objects, hostile visitors from outer space). Looking to the heavens, one saw that the earth was obviously the center of the universe, with the sun, moon, and "fixed" stars rotating, with predictable regularity, about the earth. However, there was a group of stars, the "wanderers" or "planets," that *somehow* had a kind of peculiar motion relative to the earth.

The illusion that the earth was the center was eventually explained, of course, by the heliocentric model of Nicolaus Copernicus (1473–1543). This revealed, in a beautifully simple way, that the earth and planets were *orbiting the sun.*

My second example deals with the mysterious fluid that *somehow* explained heat: When two rough surfaces slide against each other, friction squeezes out, or generates, this "heat fluid," which manifests itself as a rise in temperature.

The correct theory—which should be elevated to a law rather than a "theory"—states that the particles of matter are in vigorous motion, and the temperature of each particle is correlated with its kinetic energy of motion. This explanation is difficult to swallow, but one can actually see the incessant motion of minuscule particles—Brownian movement—with the aid of sufficient magnification via a microscope. This was a latecomer, a *botanist* looking at pollen grains [Robert Brown (1773–1858)]. Here, again, a beautifully simple explanation eventually wiped away centuries of "heat fluid."

The lesson to be learned from the above is that one should seek *simple* conjectures before surrendering to "somehow" philosophy. This entire chapter is devoted to one of the most glaring examples: Under the guise of the "uncertainty" principle, it is claimed that it is *fundamentally impossible* to explain subatomic behavior; that it is impossible to elucidate all of the present motions of a system of particles in order to predict future behavior.

Imagine that you could shrink by a factor of ten billion (in size, not calories), and walk around amongst atoms. What would the world look like? It would look like empty space. Here and there you would see some tiny wiggles, such as those of Fig. 1-1. Photons, electrons, protons, neutrons—the distinction between them becomes blurred, as they all look like diffuse wiggles. Precise position and momentum become uncertain. It is natural, therefore, that Schrodinger's quantum equations should only give probabilities. The viewpoint espoused in the present chapter is that all of this uncertainty is merely a reflection of our ignorance. "Particles" such as electrons are there, all right, but they are tiny wave packets, not compact baseballs flying around other (nuclear) baseballs.

A classical physicist, given all of the fields, positions, and momentums at $t = 0$, can calculate (in principle) an electron's position and momentum at any future time. Many quantum physicists, however, have discarded determinism. They say that only the probability of the future location, not actual location, can be determined; that, in principle, it is not possible to calculate the future whereabouts of the electron.

To repeat the definition given for determinism in Chap. 1: It is the doctrine that every event is the inevitable consequence of antecedent physical conditions. The alternative conclusion is the doctrine of "free will": For a human, it is the belief that his or her choices can be voluntary, and not determined by external causes. Now substitute "photon" or "electron" in place of "human" to fully savor the consequences of a rejection of determinism: For an electron, it is the belief that its choices can be voluntary, and not determined by external causes.

Determinism does *not* violate Heisenberg's uncertainty principle: Because the electron is a diffuse field of charge associated with a wave packet, in calculating its "future whereabouts," an approximate answer, rather than no answer at all, is to be expected.

To illustrate determinism, in the present section, the hydrogen atom is used as a vehicle for discussion. In the illustration in Fig. 2-1, an attempt is made to represent protons, electrons, and photons by means of small wiggles. Usually, however, this purism is too inconvenient if not confusing, so wave packets are represented by dots, circles (or "baseballs"), and so forth.

To bypass quantum mechanics, we should mentally get down to atomic levels. Consider again the size reduction by a factor of ten billion (10^{10}). This brings us down from a height of 2 meters to a height of 2 angstroms. It brings us to atomic and small-molecule dimensions—a water molecule, for example, has a diameter of 3 angstroms. To be "realistic," you should also imagine that time shrinks by a factor of 10^{10}. Since one second is a reasonable period of time for something significant to happen when you are 2 meters tall, what happens in 10^{-10} s (0.1 nanosecond) when you are only 2 angstroms tall?

The above mental excursions are not too farfetched. A tunneling electron microscope is able to "see" the individual molecular bumps corresponding to surface crystal structures. In the time domain, one can see individual cycles of a 10^{10} Hz (10 gigahertz) signal on a cathode-ray oscilloscope.

Returning to our imaginary angstrom-nanosecond scenario: What will a nearby hydrogen atom "look" like? As depicted in Fig. 2-1(a), we have a proton core surrounded by an electron that is, very approximately, in a circular orbit.

Are protons and electrons made out of "solid" material? Highly unlikely, for one could then cut them, like pieces of cheese, into infinitesimally small bits of matter. It is therefore conjectured that protons and electrons are diffuse fields of charge. For now, for convenience, as depicted in Fig. 2-1, the field of charge is shown as a small wave bump: a positive

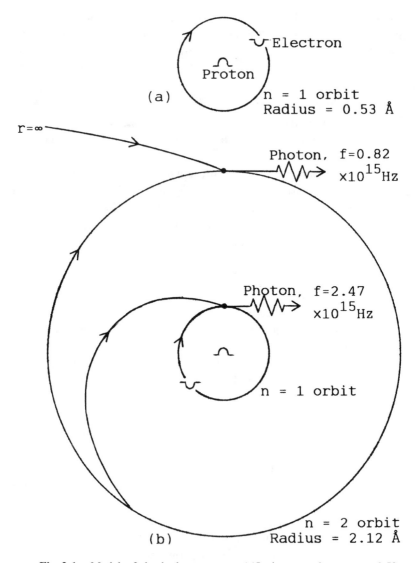

Fig. 2-1. Model of the hydrogen atom: (a)In its ground state, $r = 0.53$ angstrom (Å), the $n = 1$ orbit. (b)One of the many possible scenarios that result in photon emission. The central proton captures an electron, bringing it from $r = \infty$ to 2.12 Å, the $n = 2$ orbit. The excess energy is released in the form of a photon, $f = 0.82 \times 10^{15}$ Hz. The electron eventually spirals to the $n = 1$ orbit; the excess energy is released in the form of a photon, $f = 2.47 \times 10^{15}$ Hz.

bump ⟋⟍ for a proton, a negative bump U for an electron, and the two combined into ⊖ for a neutron. These particles may have an effective diameter but, with our present-day detection methods, it has not been possible to measure the "exact" diameter of a proton, electron, or neutron.

2-2. Planetary Motion

Fortunately, some of the concepts from the world with which we are familiar can be carried over to the atomic world. For example, planetary motion: The force of attraction between a planet in stable orbit, and the sun, has to equal the centrifugal force. (The orbits of both planets and atom electrons are only approximately circular, but in what follows idealized conditions are assumed, with circular orbits around a stationary sun or atomic nucleus.)

Let us assume, for the sake of a reasonably simple model, that the planet starts out very far away from the sun; i.e., the center-to-center distance from the sun, r, is very large. Because of this, the time for one revolution around the circular orbit, a "year," is also relatively large. Nevertheless, the planet has been captured, and it slowly spirals in toward the sun. (Will the earth and Jupiter and all of the other planets eventually fall into the sun? Theoretically, yes, but the sun is scheduled to become unstable in "only" 5 billion years, well before any of the planets spiral into the solar corona.)

As the planet approaches the sun, its velocity increases, so it gains kinetic energy—the energy of motion. As an example, in Table 1-2, we are given for the present-day earth mass $m = 5.974 \times 10^{24}$ kilograms, sun's mass $M = 1.988 \times 10^{30}$ kilograms, earth's center-to-center distance from the sun $r = 1.496 \times 10^{11}$ meters, so that the earth's kinetic energy is 2.649×10^{33} joules. This would be converted into heat if, somehow, the earth could be "stopped dead." (The masses are, of course, calculated, based on precise laboratory measurements of gravitational attraction.)

Energy is the ability to do work. The planet, in approaching the sun from very far away ($r = \infty$) to its present r, has already done work, so its potential energy is negative. It turns out that the *magnitude* of the potential energy is twice that of the kinetic energy. Thus, the earth's potential energy, or ability to do work relative to its position at $r = \infty$, is -5.297×10^{33} joules. Exactly half of the potential energy, the above 2.649×10^{33} joules, has been converted into the earth's kinetic energy of motion. What happened to the other half? It has been converted into heat (mostly tidal friction) as it spiraled in toward the sun.

The tide on earth caused by the pull of the sun is relatively small. The tidal component due to the pull of the moon is comparatively large, and represents a huge ever-present conversion into heat. It is one of the important renewable sources of energy, renewable in the sense that it will take a relatively long time for the moon to complete its spiral journey into the earth. (At the present time, because of certain complex interactions, it seems to be moving away from the earth. There is plenty of geological evidence to show that the moon's rotation around the earth has not always been $30 \times 24 = 720$ hours long, and the earth's daily rotation on its axis has not always been 24 hours long.) It is a simple matter to calculate how fast the moon will be going if and when it strikes the earth; the splash is guaranteed to be spectacular!

2-3. Hydrogen Atom's Electron Motion

What does planetary motion have in common with electron motion? Some of the equations are similar—for example, the equations for kinetic and potential energy. The orbital radii are, however, different. A planet can have any orbital radius (until it grazes the sun's surface, of course). For the hydrogen atom, however, only integer values of n (that is, $n = 1, 2, 3, \ldots$, also called the quantum number) are allowed. The lowest state of energy corresponds to $n = 1$, and so forth. We get, for the $n = 1$ orbit of Fig. 2-1(a), $r_1 = 5.292 \times 10^{-11}$ meter. It is convenient to multiply by 10^{10}, which gives the radius in angstroms:

$$r_1 = 0.5292 \text{ angstrom} = 0.5292 \text{ Å}.$$

If you remember that a water molecule (H_2O) has a diameter of 3 Å, you can easily visualize its two hydrogen nuclei with their electrons flying about at a radius of 0.5292 Å (but this is highly oversimplified because it ignores interactions between the hydrogen and oxygen atoms).

How fast is the electron "flying about" its hydrogen nucleus? For $n = 1$, we get for the frequency of the first orbit, the number of rotations per second,

$$f_1 = 6.580 \times 10^{15} \text{ Hz}.$$

As Table 1-1 shows, this value falls into the ultraviolet range. However, the electrons orbit in silence; they do not radiate at this frequency. (If they did, a flask of hydrogen gas would have an ultraviolet "color.")

We may be familiar with the effects of ultraviolet light, but are completely unfamiliar with something that goes around in a circle some 10^{15}

times a second. A human lifetime occupies 2.5×10^9 seconds (to age 80). Beyond that threshold, a value one million times greater is beyond comprehension (we could also be talking about the national debt). It is obvious that, in one second, the hydrogen electron has plenty of time to visit all regions of its local surrounding space in accordance with Schrodinger's probability equations.

Another example in which "determinism" defines the future when an electron changes its orbit is depicted in Fig. 2-1(b). Here the hydrogen proton has captured an electron, at $r = \infty$, and brought it to the allowed orbit at $n = 2$. The radius is 2.117 Å, and orbital frequency is 0.8225×10^{15} Hz. (This happens to also be the frequency of the photon that is released.)

For a hydrogen electron, instead of gravitational attraction, we have electrostatic attraction. Instead of the sun of mass M and a planet of mass m gravitationally pulling on each other, we have a proton of charge $+e$ and an electron of charge $-e$ electrostatically pulling on each other. The result is, for the hydrogen electron in the $n = 2$ orbit, kinetic energy $= 0.5450 \times 10^{-18}$ joule. The hydrogen electron's potential energy, in the $n = 2$ orbit, is -1.0899×10^{-18} joule, negative because the electron has already done work in approaching the proton from $r = \infty$ to its present r. Exactly as is the case for planetary motion, the *magnitude* of the potential energy is twice that of the kinetic energy.

We see that half of the potential energy has been converted into the electron's kinetic energy. What happened to the other half? As portrayed in Fig. 2-1(b), when the electron spirals to the $n = 2$ orbit from $n = \infty$, it releases the excess energy by launching a photon. The numerical values for the electron's energy at $n = 2$ are

$$E_{\text{electron}} = E_{\text{kinetic}} + E_{\text{potential}} = (0.5450 - 1.0899)10^{-18}$$
$$= -0.5450 \times 10^{-18} \text{ joule.}$$

The photon's frequency is given by Planck's law,

$$\text{Photon frequency } (f) = \frac{\text{Photon energy } (E_{\text{ph}})}{\text{Planck's constant } (h)}.$$

[Planck's constant is named after Max Planck (1858–1947).] Numerical values yield

$$f = \frac{0.5450 \times 10^{-18}}{6.6261 \times 10^{-34}} = 8.225 \times 10^{14} \text{ Hz}$$

(ultraviolet range). These photons are detected as one of the prominent frequencies radiated by excited hydrogen atoms. The recoil after the electron launches the photon is exactly the correct amount to leave it in the $n = 2$ orbit.

Although the $n = 2$ orbit is allowed, is it stable? This depends on one's viewpoint. Something that does not change for several million cycles would seem to be stable. According to Schrodinger's equations, although some of the probabilities may be very small, the electron eventually visits every bit of its $n = 2$ allowed volume. Typically, after several million cycles, the electron is overwhelmed by instability and heads for the $n = 1$ orbit. This is shown as a sharp spiral in Fig. 2-1(b), but the actual path may be relatively gradual. (In quantum language, however, the orbital change is called an instantaneous quantum jump.)

As illustrated, the electron launches a photon when it reaches the $n = 1$ orbit, and the recoil allows it to stably enter the orbit. The easiest way to find the frequency of the new photon is to calculate the difference in energy levels. The numerical value for the electron's energy at $n = 1$ is

$$E_{electron} = E_{kinetic} + E_{potential} = (2.180 - 4.360)10^{-18}$$
$$= -2.180 \times 10^{-18} \text{ joule.}$$

Therefore, in changing its orbit, the electron has done work amounting to

$$2.180 - 0.545 = 1.635 \ (\times 10^{-18}) \text{ joule,}$$

so Planck's law yields

$$f = 2.467 \times 10^{15} \text{ Hz}$$

(ultraviolet range). This is the lowest frequency of what is known as the Lyman series. It happens to be exactly three times the frequency of the photon released at $n = 2$.

Another "deterministic" way for the electron to be dislodged from its $n = 2$ orbit is to hit it with a photon, in synchronism with many other excited hydrogen atoms, in a laser tube. LASER is an acronym for light amplification by stimulated emission of radiation, which very well describes the process.

2-4. Radioactive Decay

Finally, let us consider radioactive decay. For example, a uranium U^{238} nucleus contains 92 protons and 146 neutrons, for a total of 238 mass particles. All of the residents of the nucleus, whether they are protons or neutrons, are called *nucleons*. The "cross-section" through a U^{238} nucleus is schematically shown in Fig. 2-2.

The element has a half-life of 4.51 billion years; that is, starting with a pure sample of U^{238}, half of it will undergo spontaneous fission (it will violently fall apart) in 4.51×10^9 years (which can also be expressed as $10^{9.654}$ years).

The diameter of a nucleus is, of course, much smaller than that of an atom. The uranium nucleus has a diameter of 13.6×10^{-15} m $= 0.000136$ angstrom $= 13.6$ femtometers $= 13.6$ fm. In other words, we would have to shrink ourselves by a factor of 10^{15} to become comparable to nuclei.

The nucleus is bound together by the *strong* or *nuclear interaction* force. This is different from gravitational and electromagnetic forces, and it overwhelms the repulsion between like charges (positive protons) provided the distance is less than 1.4 fm. This latter value is the range over which the strong force operates; it rapidly decreases to zero beyond this radius. (Needless to say, we have no idea as to what the strong force is, any more than we know what gravitational, magnetic, or electrostatic forces

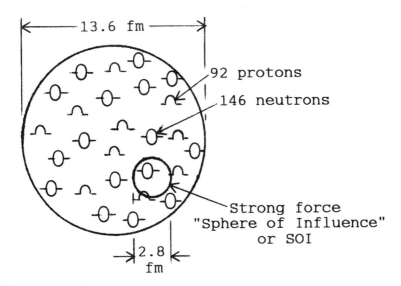

Fig. 2-2.   "Cross-section" through a uranium U^{238} nucleus. There are 92 protons and 146 neutrons for a total of 238 nucleons. The diameter is 13.6×10^{-15} m $= 13.6$ femtometers $= 13.6$ fm. Also shown is the "sphere of influence," or SOI, of the strong force, which rapidly decreases to zero beyond a radius of 1.4 fm.

are, but the strong force solved the mystery of what holds the nucleus together if all of those protons are repelling each other.)

Despite the difficulties we have in observing these approximate
spheres of femtometer diameters, the picture that emerges is the following:
The protons and neutrons are in rapid motion, interacting little with each
other. The movements are approximately independent because of the short
range of the strong force. Electrostatic repulsion is a relatively weak contribution, and temperature is not a factor in radioactive decay. (The goings-
on in a nucleus are shielded from the outside jostling between atoms, which
is the basis of "temperature" to us.)

For the U^{238} nucleus, Fig. 2-2 suggests the following: Its volume is
given by

1300 cubic femtometers,

while the volume of each strong force's sphere of influence, or SOI, is

11.49 cubic femtometers.

According to the volume ratio, we can model the nucleus as a sphere divided into 115.4 SOIs. In other words, visualize that the uranium nucleus
consists of 115.4 different regions, each having a diameter of around 2.8
femtometers (or volume of 11.49 cubic femtometers). Since there is a total of 238 nucleons, but only 115.4 SOIs, many of these SOIs will contain
two or even three nucleons at a given time.

What is the cause-and-effect that leads a U^{238} nucleus to disintegrate
in 4.51×10^9 years? (Although only half do so, it is convenient in what follows to refer to the nucleus that fissions in *exactly* 4.51×10^9 years.) Because of their movements, the 92 protons and 146 neutrons occupy a
different distribution of SOIs from moment to moment. Many of these distributions are unstable: most notably, if approximately 46 protons and 73
neutrons accumulate near one "side" of the nucleus, while the remaining
half accumulate near the opposite side, this encourages a dumbbell-like
shape. The nucleus splits apart near the middle of the dumbbell, and the
two daughter nuclei fly apart. The daughters may be unstable, and not
every unstable nucleus falls apart via the dumbbell route, but the general
explanation is the same: for radioactive nuclei, an unstable configuration
of nucleons eventually occurs.

Is it reasonable for the U^{238} nucleus to fall apart after $4.51 \times
10^9$ years of togetherness? A few simple calculations show how this can
come about.

   In what follows, we will witness a battle between exponents. We start out with deceptively small numbers: The U^{238} nucleus contains 92 protons, 146 neutrons, and 115.4 SOIs. First, consider the 92 protons. In how many ways can they distribute themselves over the 115.4 SOIs? Because of the mutual repulsion between protons, it is reasonable to assume that there will be a maximum of one per SOI. Therefore, if we line up the SOIs from left to right, the distributions can extend from

$$P\;P\;P\;.\;.\;.\;.\;.\;.\;P\;P\;P\;0\;0\;0\;.\;.\;.\;0\;0\;0$$

$$\overset{\longleftarrow\!\!-\!\!-\!\!-\!\!-\!\!92\!\!-\!\!-\!\!-\!\!-\!\!\longrightarrow}{}\quad\overset{\longleftarrow\!\!-\!\!23.4\!\!-\!\!\longrightarrow}{}$$

$$\overset{\longleftarrow\!\!-\!\!-\!\!-\!\!-\!\!-\!\!-\!\!-\!\!115.4\!\!-\!\!-\!\!-\!\!-\!\!-\!\!-\!\!-\!\!\longrightarrow}{}$$

to

$$0\;0\;0\;.\;.\;.\;0\;0\;0\;P\;P\;P\;.\;.\;.\;.\;.\;.\;P\;P\;P$$

$$\overset{\longleftarrow\!\!-\!\!23.4\!\!-\!\!\longrightarrow}{}\quad\overset{\longleftarrow\!\!-\!\!-\!\!-\!\!-\!\!92\!\!-\!\!-\!\!-\!\!-\!\!\longrightarrow}{}$$

The top row represents an extreme condition in which the first 92 SOIs contain a proton, while the remaining 23.4 SOIs do not contain a proton. The bottom row represents the extreme in which the last 92 SOIs contain a proton, and so forth. Of course, any in-between combination is possible. The most stable distribution would look like

$$P\;P\;P\;P\;0\;P\;P\;P\;P\;0\;P\;P\;.\;.\;.\;.\;P\;P\;0\;P\;P\;P\;P\;0\;P\;P\;P\;P$$

$$\overset{\longleftarrow\!\!-\!\!-\!\!-\!\!-\!\!-\!\!-\!\!-\!\!115.4\!\!-\!\!-\!\!-\!\!-\!\!-\!\!-\!\!-\!\!\longrightarrow}{}$$

because there are approximately four Ps to every 0.
   How many combinations are possible? Any elementary algebra book should give the number of different combinations of n elements taken r at a time as

$$C(n,r) = \frac{n!}{r!(n-r)!}.$$

Considering the huge number of combinations that are possible, this is a surprisingly simple (and useful) equation. It is illustrated in the following example: Given $n=5$ elements taken $r=3$ at a time; i.e., we have a nucleus that contains 3 protons distributed over 5 SOIs. The answer is

$$C(5,3) = \frac{5!}{3!2!} = \frac{120}{6 \times 2} = 10.$$

Here are the 10 combinations:

```
P P P 0 0
P P 0 P 0
P P 0 0 P
P 0 P P 0
P 0 P 0 P
P 0 0 P P
0 P P P 0
0 P P 0 P
0 P 0 P P
0 0 P P P
```

(The standard trick in writing this is to substitute 1 for P, and list in descending numerical order.)

Returning to the uranium nucleus, we have $n = 115.4$ SOIs and $r = 92$ protons. Therefore, the protons in the U^{238} nucleus can form the following number of combinations:

$$C_P = \frac{115.4!}{92!\,23.4!} = \frac{10^{189.4}}{10^{142.1}10^{23.0}} = 10^{24.3}.$$

This is a huge number of combinations: 1 followed by 24 zeros. Because of symmetries, the effective value is somewhat less than indicated. Also, current nuclear theory says that the protons and neutrons tend to form concentric "shells", similar to the electron shells that surround the nucleus, so there is not a completely chaotic mixture of protons and neutrons. In what follows, however, the effects of symmetries and shells will be ignored. The final conclusion, that there is a huge number of combinations, remains valid.

Next, consider the 146 neutrons. In how many ways can they distribute themselves over the 115.4 SOIs? Despite the strong force, neutrons (and protons) are kept apart by their incessant and rapid motion. It is reasonable to assume that, at a given instant, there will be one neutron per SOI, plus 30.6 wandering leftovers. Therefore, if the SOIs are lined up from left to right, the distributions can extend from

```
N N N        N N N
                       N N N · · · · · · N N N
                · · ·
N N N        N N N
  ←———30.6———→   ←———————84.8———————→
  ←———————————115.4———————————→
```

to

$$
\begin{array}{cc}
& N\,N\,N \cdot \cdot \cdot N\,N\,N \\
N\,N\,N \cdot \cdot \cdot \cdot \cdot \cdot N\,N\,N & \\
& N\,N\,N \cdot \cdot \cdot N\,N\,N
\end{array}
$$

$$\longleftarrow\!\!\!-\!\!\!-84.8\!\!\!-\!\!\!-\!\!\!\longrightarrow \quad \longleftarrow\!\!\!-\!\!\!-30.6\!\!\!-\!\!\!\longrightarrow$$

The upper group represents an extreme condition in which the first 30.6 SOIs contain two neutrons, while the remaining 84.8 SOIs contain a single neutron, and so forth. The most stable distribution would look like

$$
\begin{array}{cccccc}
N & N & N & & N & N \\
N\,N\,N & N\,N\,N & N \cdot \cdot \cdot \cdot N & N\,N\,N & N\,N\,N \\
N & N & N & & N & N
\end{array}
$$

$$\longleftarrow\!\!\!-\!\!\!-\!\!\!-\!\!\!-\!\!\!-\!\!\!-\!\!\!-115.4\!\!\!-\!\!\!-\!\!\!-\!\!\!-\!\!\!-\!\!\!-\!\!\!-\!\!\!\longrightarrow$$

because there are approximately three Ns to every $\dfrac{N}{N}$.

According to the above, the 30.6 neutrons can form the following number of combinations:

$$C_N = \frac{115.4!}{30.6!\,84.8!} = \frac{10^{189.4}}{10^{33.2}10^{128.2}} = 10^{27.9}.$$

Finally, we end up with a huge monster exponent: Nucleus "togetherness" is one in which the family members largely ignore each other. We can assume that the proton and neutron distributions are independent. If that is the case, *each* of the proton distributions can be combined with *all* of the neutron distributions, and vice versa. The grand total number of proton and neutron combinations is the *product* of the individual number of combinations, or

$$C_{P+N} = 10^{52.2}.$$

It turns out that the U^{238} nucleus cannot even come close to $10^{52.2}$ combinations in 4.51 billion years: How many *seconds* are there in 4.51×10^9 years?

$$60 \times 60 \times 24 \times 365 \times 4.51 \times 10^9 = 10^{17.15}.$$

How many different combinations can occur in the nucleus each second? Let us go from the sublime to the ridiculous: Assume, although we know that it is impossible, that a nucleon can move from one SOI to an adjacent SOI, a center-to-center distance of 2.8 fm, at the speed of light. The time taken to traverse this distance is

$$\frac{2.8 \times 10^{-15}}{3 \times 10^8} = 10^{-23.03} \text{ second.}$$

In 4.51 billion years, therefore, there would be

$$\frac{10^{17.15}}{10^{-23.03}} = 10^{40.2}$$

movements—not even close to the total number of possible combinations, $10^{52.2}$.

The above implies that there are many SOI combinations that *probably* result in spontaneous fission. The main point of the above exercise is this: It also implies that the fields, positions, and momentums of the nucleons at $t = 0$ *determine* how and when the nucleus will fission $10^{9.654}$ years later. Perhaps 10^{20} computer hackers, working for 10^{10} years, can come up with the numerical answers that will convert these *probablies* into certainties.

Chapter 3

The Photon Model

3-1. A Sound Wave

To repeat a comment made in Chap. 1: The most well-known example that strains quantum reality is a sensational experiment that involves photons. It forms the basis for the present chapter.

A typical electromagnetic field (EMF) is the macroscopic integration of billions of photons. If the EMF is sufficiently attenuated, however, it displays its individual photons, and we can actually detect these individual wavelets. In other words, a photon is the irreducible constituent of an EMF. It is a tiny wave packet (see Fig. 1-1) whose frequency is the same as that of the parent EMF.

A photon is a form of energy; the relation between its frequency f and energy E_{ph} is described by Planck's law (previously given in Chap. 2):

$$f = \frac{E_{ph}}{h}$$

where h is Planck's constant. The summation of energies contained in the individual photon wave packets has to, of course, equal the energy in the "parent" EMF.

It is good strategy, in the present chapter, to review certain characteristics of an electromagnetic wave. Because some of these are descriptive of *any* wave, the discussion is reinforced if we first consider a wave that is completely different in many respects—that of sound. Despite the differences, however, the characteristics of sound and EMF propagation can be presented in the *same* table, Table 3-1.

Another reason for considering sound is that it is a longitudinal vibration [the molecules (of air, say) vibrate back-and-forth in the same direction that the wave travels]; in discussing the wave-particle duality field of a photon, and of an electron in Chap. 4, it is possible that these fields are longitudinal. It is helpful to mentally prepare ourselves for the possibility that not every field is transverse—that is, not every field has lines that are oriented at right angles to the direction in which the wave travels.

An electromagnetic wave is transverse, it is transmitted without losses through a vacuum, and it travels at the speed of light (by definition) in a vacuum. By contrast a sound wave, illustrated in Fig. 3-1, is longitudinal, it is transmitted through matter (gas, liquid, or solid), and the velocity of propagation is relatively slow. However, both waves are analogous with regard to the equations for the velocity of propagation (v_s or v) and characteristic impedance (Z_0).

Table 3-1. Analogies between sound and an electromagnetic field (EMF). Air and water are at a pressure of 760 mm Hg, temperature of 0°C. Symbols stand for the following:

$$\rho_D = \text{density, kilogram/cubic meter;}$$
$$Y_0 = \text{modulus of elasticity, pascal;}$$
$$v_s, v = \text{velocity, meter/second;}$$
$$Z_0 = \text{characteristic impedance, ohm;}$$
$$\mu = \text{permeability, henry/meter;}$$
$$\epsilon = \text{permittivity, farad/meter}$$

	Given values		Derived values	
Sound	ρ_D, kg/m³	Y_0, Pa	v_s, m/s	Z_0, Ω
Air	1.297	1.425×10^5	331	430
Water	992	0.232×10^{10}	1529	1.517×10^6
Nickel	8700	20×10^{10}	4795	4.171×10^7
EMF	μ, H/m	$1/\epsilon$, m/F	v, m/s	Z_0, Ω
Vacuum-air	1.257×10^{-6}	11.29×10^{10}	2.998×10^8	376.7
Ruby mica	1.257×10^{-6}	2.092×10^{10}	1.290×10^8	162.1
Water	1.257×10^{-6}	0.1448×10^{10}	0.339×10^8	42.66

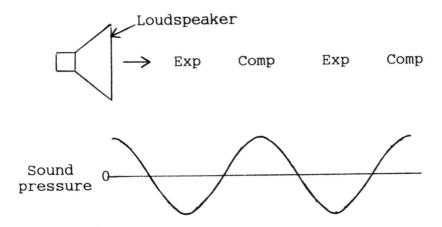

Fig. 3-1.   Expansions and compressions of a longitudinal sound wave.

What is characteristic impedance? It informs us how well a signal can be transmitted from one medium to another without suffering a loss due to reflection. For example, because of the huge difference in the Z_0 of air and water (430 versus 1,517,000), an underwater swimmer is shielded from sound in the air above. The sound is almost completely reflected back, as if the water surface is a mirror. For a visible-light wave striking a mirror, the situation is more complicated because the reflecting surface is an electrical conductor (silver or aluminum). Nevertheless, the idea is the same: At the sharp discontinuity between air (or glass) and the silver or aluminum coating, visible-frequency EMFs are almost completely reflected.

For sound, the velocity v_s is determined by Y_0 (Young's modulus of the medium), and ρ_D (density of the medium). Young's modulus is the stress/strain; i.e., given a cube of the material, with one side of the cube in the form of a piston, we apply a force and divide by the movement of the piston. The stress has the units of newtons/square meter; the strain is the change in thickness (meters) divided by the original thickness (meters), so the strain is "dimensionless"—it is a fraction, without units. Then Y_0 has the units of newtons/square meter, which is shortened to the pascal, symbol Pa.

One can think of Young's modulus, also called the modulus of elasticity, as a measure of the stiffness of the material. Table 3-1 lists Y_0 for three common and representative materials: air, water, and nickel. Young's modulus is relatively small for air, of course. We see that water, frequently cited as "incompressible," is much more compressible than a metal such as nickel.

The density affects the velocity because the movements associated with the compressions and expansions of the medium, in Fig. 3-1, are opposed by its inertia. At one extreme Table 3-1 lists air, which has low density, high compressibility, and low velocity (331 m/s). At the other extreme, nickel has high density, low compressibility, and high velocity (4795 m/s). Water falls in between.

3-2. Electromagnetic Field

For the EMF, only the simplest example, that of a plane wave, is considered below. Accordingly, in the end view of Fig. 3-2, the EMF consists of vertical electric ($\underline{E}$) and horizontal magnetic ($\underline{H}$) fields that are mutually at right angles to each other and to the direction of propagation. The "mutually at right angles to each other" defines a plane wave. Why is it necessary to have such a complicated drawing for the EMF when the simple diagram of Fig. 3-1 suffices for sound? We can get away with Fig. 3-1 because sound is much simpler—it is a one-dimensional vibration in the direction of propagation. Also, it is important to get the full flavor of an EMF before we break it down into its minuscule constituents, photons such as that of Fig. 1-1.

In order to show the $\underline{E}$ and $\underline{H}$ fields, Fig. 3-2 uses a waveguide, which is conveniently chosen to be two wavelengths long, to propagate the EMF. The waveguide is a hollow rectangular bar made out of a good conductor (to minimize electrical losses). To the EMF signal, however, the waveguide is much more than a hollow bar. As the lower side view shows, the upper and lower walls of the waveguide look like inductances L (symbolized by coils of "wire"); at the same time, the upper and lower walls form capacitances C (symbolized by parallel plates). The Ls and Cs are actually distributed elements; one cannot look at the hollow bar and point to specific Ls and Cs, because all tiny lengths of the waveguide are identical, and each represents a minuscule L and C. However, it is convenient to regard the Ls and Cs as discrete lumped elements that are located at the zero crossover points of the $\underline{E}$ and $\underline{H}$ fields, as they show up in our imaginary "photograph" at this instant of time.

The "photograph" of Fig. 3-2 shows four parameters at this particular instant of time: $\underline{E}$, $\underline{H}$, V, and I:

$\underline{H}$: The magnetic fields ($\underline{H}$) alternate as shown in the top view.

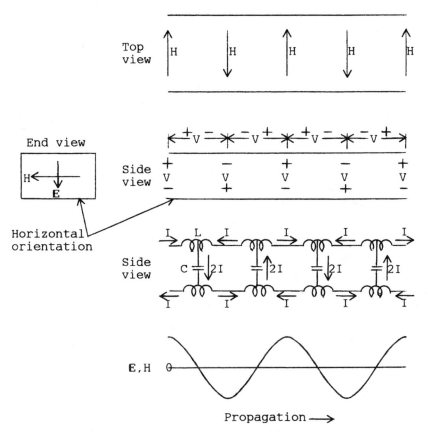

Fig. 3-2. "Photograph," taken at a particular instant of time, of the electromagnetic field (EMF) associated with a waveguide. Although the
Ls and Cs formed by the walls are distributed, it is more convenient to show them as discrete elements that are located at the zero
crossover points of the electric ($\underline{E}$) and magnetic ($\underline{H}$) fields. The
$\underline{E}$ and $\underline{H}$ fields are mutually at right angles to each other and to the
direction of propagation.

V: In the upper side view, there are two sets of *V*s. The vertical $\pm$, ...,
set is the voltage between top and bottom walls of the waveguide. The electric ($\underline{E}$) fields are these voltages divided by the height of the waveguide,
so the units of $\underline{E}$ are volts/meter.

The horizontal $+-$, $-+$, ... set of *V*s is the voltage along the top
wall (the voltage along the bottom wall, not shown, is $-+$, $+-$, ...). These

voltages are caused by currents I, shown in the lower side view, flowing through the inductances L.

There is a second set of currents—the vertical $2I$ discharges of capacitances C, in the lower side view.

The Vs and Is actually form continuous sinusoidal distributions, like the $\underline{E},\underline{H}$ wave, but are shown lumped for the sake of clarity.

Notice how, in the lower side view, the Is form loops similar to those of one-turn transformers. Each of these loops generates the magnetic field intensity, $\underline{H}$. The units of $\underline{H}$ are amperes/meter.

The expression "polarized light" has become quite commonplace, but polarization applies to all EMFs in general, not only to light waves. The direction of polarization is, by definition, the same as the direction of the $\underline{E}$ field. In Fig. 3-2, therefore, we have vertical polarization. The direction of polarization is one of the important characteristics of an EMF and, by extension, of a photon.

When the EMF emerges into vacuum (or air), at the right end of the waveguide, the $\underline{E}$ and $\underline{H}$ lines remain mutually perpendicular to each other and to the direction of propagation. At the edges, however, unrestrained by waveguide walls, the EMF beam laterally spreads out (diffraction). Because $\underline{E}$ and $\underline{H}$ lines have to be continuous, what happens to the ends of the fields after they leave the waveguide? The positive ends of one $\underline{E}$ line join up with the negative ends of the adjacent $\underline{E}$ lines to form an ever-expanding zig-zag pattern as the beam spreads out. The same joining-up of the ends of adjacent lines occurs for the $\underline{H}$ field diffraction.

Returning to Table 3-1: For EMF propagation, the characteristics of three representative mediums are listed: vacuum-air, ruby mica, and water (distilled). What is analogous to the Young's modulus and density that we have in sound transmission? The answer is found in the Ls and Cs of the waveguide. Inductance is associated with opposition to changing current, analogous to the inertia of mass. The magnetic permeability, μ, is analogous to density, ρ_D. Capacitance is associated with ease of charge, analogous to elasticity. The medium's permittivity, ε, is analogous to the reciprocal of stiffness, $1/Y_0$ (or ε is analogous to mechanical compressibility).

The three EMF mediums of Table 3-1 are nonmagnetic, so each has the same permeability, $\mu = 4\pi \times 10^{-7} = 1.257 \times 10^{-6}$ henrys/meter. The reciprocal of permittivity, $1/\varepsilon$, is listed. For vacuum-air, the value is $1/\varepsilon = 1/8.8542 \times 10^{-12} = 1.129 \times 10^{11}$ meters/farad. [For ruby mica and water, the $1/\varepsilon$ values are reduced (divided) by their dielectric constants, respectively 5.4 and 78.]

For an EMF, the velocity is determined by permeability μ and permittivity ε. For vacuum-air, we of course get $v = c = 2.998 \times 10^8$ m/s, and a characteristic impedance of $Z_0 = 376.7$ ohms is obtained, as listed. Since Z_0 for ruby mica and water is different from that of vacuum-air, an EMF traveling from air to mica, or from air to water, is partially reflected (and partially transmitted) at the boundary between the dissimilar mediums.

An important specification of a photon is its energy, since this gives the frequency via Planck's law. This ties in with an EMF signal because electric and magnetic fields are forms of energy. Aside from its minuscule magnitude, the main difference between a photon and the EMF of Fig. 3-2 is that the latter is a steady-state sinusoidal signal. Its energy is given in joules per second (which equals power in watts), whereas the energy of a photon is given in joules. The EMF in Fig. 3-2 has a certain power density in watts/square meter. This is the *total* power density carried through the waveguide by the EMF; we do not say that half of this is due to the $\underline{E}$ field and the other half to the $\underline{H}$ field, because $\underline{E}$ and $\underline{H}$ are inseparable. (The magnetic field of the earth exists without an $\underline{E}$ field, and the electric field of a battery exists without an $\underline{H}$ field, but these fields are not propagating. Figure 3-2 illustrates a signal, like the one leaving a radio transmitter, that is traveling at the speed of light.)

Photons ignore each other; they do not interact in the same way that electrons do, for example, since electrons repel each other because of their like (minus) charges. But photons *do* interact in a different sense. A single, isolated photon reveals itself by tiny $\underline{E}$ and $\underline{H}$ lines. (Individual lines do not actually exist, of course, but they are a very convenient manmade concept for visualization and design.) In a laser beam, the edge of one photon's $\underline{E}$ and $\underline{H}$ lines join up with the next, and many $\underline{E}$ and $\underline{H}$ lines coincide, so the net effect is that of a huge universe of $\underline{E}$ and $\underline{H}$ lines, and we get the waveguide fields of Fig. 3-2.

3-3. Two-Slit Interference Pattern

As a strategy for studying the photon, we start out, innocently enough, with the relatively strong EMF output of a laser, and then attenuate the field until individual photons can be isolated. Truly strange and unbelievable happenings are then observed.

As a vehicle for this discussion, consider the two-slit (sometimes called double-slit) diffraction-interference apparatus of Fig. 3-3(a). The

EMF, polarized with the $\underline{E}$ lines in the plane of the page, as shown, is propagating to the right. It strikes an opaque plate that contains two slits (they are at right angles to the page). Some of the EMF gets through the upper slit, and some through the lower slit.

The effects exploited here are used in many different applications; an especially fruitful area is that of astronomy. The two words—diffraction and interference—may be ominous, but the idea is really very simple, and that is why it works so well. We are dealing here with sine waves, such as the $\underline{E}$ and $\underline{H}$ waveforms of Fig. 3-2. When the laser beam sine wave of Fig. 3-3(a) passes through a narrow slit, it spreads out laterally—it diffracts—so that light passing through each slit spreads over the photo-

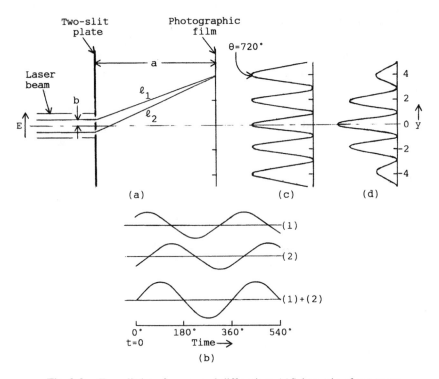

Fig. 3-3. Two-slit interference and diffraction: (a)Schematic of apparatus. The slits are at right angles to the page. Two of the rays leaving the slits are depicted as they meet at $y = 4$ of the photographic film. (b)Waveforms of rays (1) and (2) when they meet at the film if they are 90° out of phase. (c)Idealized film pattern. (d)The film pattern "corrected" by adding the attenuation that accompanies diffraction.

graphic film at the right. The film intercepts light extending from $y = -5$ to $y = +5$, as shown by the vertical scale of Fig. 3-3(d).

The second word—interference—is misleading, but it is too late for us to change it. "Interference" implies that the two rays emerging from the slits act to hinder or impede each other. This is fine for football, but in Fig. 3-3(a), half of the time, the two rays aid each other (constructive interference). This seems to be a good example of an oxymoron. The process in which the two rays hinder each other is called "destructive interference."

Two of the rays thus formed, (1) of length ℓ_1, and (2) of length ℓ_2, are singled out as they come together on the sheet of photographic film. (Visible or ultraviolet light is usually used because their photons have sufficient energy to be recorded on the film.) What pattern will the exposed film show?

In some locations, the EMF from ray (1) is in-phase with that of ray (2) when they meet at the film, thus increasing film exposure (constructive interference). At other locations, they have opposite phases, and the EMFs cancel (destructive interference). Figure 3-3(b) illustrates an in-between situation in which they are 90° out-of-phase; there is some increase in total output, by a factor of 1.414. The net results of constructive and destructive interference are the idealized set of peaks and valleys of Fig. 3-3(c).

Rays ℓ_1 and ℓ_2 are shown with relative values (as defined in Fig. 3-3):

$$b = 0.5, a = 10, y = 4,$$

(and $\theta = 720° = 4\pi$ because it is the second peak away from the $y = 0$ axis). The numerical values correspond to relative laser light wavelength $\lambda = 0.1857$. Ray ℓ_2 is 10.97 units long and contains 59 cycles of laser signal. Ray ℓ_1 is 10.59 units long and contains 57 cycles. Therefore, the two signals arrive in phase (constructive interference).

At $y = 1$, $\theta \cong 180° = \pi$, the longer path is 54.4 cycles long, the shorter path is 53.9 cycles long, so the difference is 0.5 cycle. Therefore, the two signals cancel (destructive interference).

A change has been applied to Fig. 3-3(c) to convert it into the more realistic film exposure of Fig. 3-3(d). Because diffraction is accompanied by attenuation, Fig. 3-3(c) has been multiplied by a factor of the "Gaussian" form $\exp(-ky^2)$. The numerical value $k = 0.0625$ is used to get Fig. 3-3(d). [The accurate form for Fig. 3-3(d) can be derived given the various physical and wavelength dimensions, but $\exp(-0.0625y^2)$ is a convenient assumption.]

Now consider that the EMF is a form of energy. If the EMF vanishes because of destructive interference, its energy must be picked up by regions of constructive interference. How this can come about is crudely shown in Fig. 3-4. (An exact analysis may require a high-speed computer in the hands of a thesis student, but Fig. 3-4 is adequate to illustrate the general idea.) We have three parallel EMFs propagating to the right: upper, middle, and lower. The numerical values give $\underline{E}$ field intensities. For some reason, such as destructive interference, the middle path is attenuated: $\underline{E} = 100, 80, 60, \ldots$, until it vanishes at the right. Notice that the $\underline{E}$ lines alternate (up, down, up, . . .) as they do in Fig. 3-2. This determines the other values because (1) the $\underline{E}$ lines have to be continuous, and (2) the algebraic summation at each junction has to be zero. The net result is that the $\underline{E}$ lines become distorted, as shown, with substantial increases in upper and lower constructive-interference paths.

From the photon's point of view: A photon is a form of energy, $E = fh$. It travels at right angles to its $\underline{E}$ (and $\underline{H}$) lines. After each photon gets past the double slits, it diffracts by an amount that is based on its predetermined

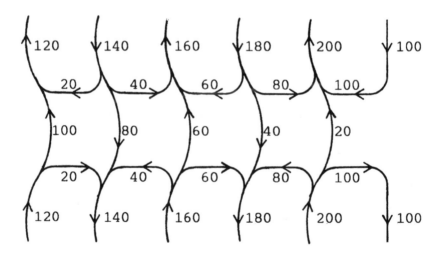

Propagation ⟶

Fig. 3-4.   Crude depiction of $\underline{E}$ field intensities if EMF is propagating to the right, with destructive interference in the middle path, but with constructive interference in the upper and lower paths. Because of the interaction between concave and convex lines, photons are directed toward regions of constructive interference.

but statistically random prior experiences. Because of the bending of the $\underline{E}$ lines in Fig. 3-4, entering photons veer off toward the upper and lower paths, avoiding the middle destructive-interference path. When a photon strikes the photographic film, its energy is released, exposing a small dot (diameter approximately equal to the photon's wavelength).

In other words, in Fig. 3-3(a), the photons actually curve away from destructive-interference points $y = \pm1$ and ±3, and toward constructive-interference points $y = 0, \pm2$, and ±4. As a result of this "curving away," the valleys of Fig. 3-3(c) and (d) are created.

3-4. Simultaneous-Burst Pattern

Our next step is to carefully decrease the output of the laser beam. Suppose that an ideally fast shutter allows a burst of only 1000 photons to *simultaneously* fly through the slits. We are immediately faced with probabilities. Around 500 photons will probably pass through the upper slit, the remaining approximately 500 through the lower slit. Their $\underline{E}$ and $\underline{H}$ fields join up, $+$ to $-$, as they laterally disperse via diffraction.

Experiments show that the film exposure display of Fig. 3-3(d) occurs independent of laser beam intensity (but not much, if anything, will be visible if there is a total of only 1000 photons).

In order to refer to specific numerical values, a distribution diagram is shown in Fig. 3-5(a). First, the $\exp(-ky^2)$ values at $y = 0, \pm0.5, \pm1, \ldots,$ ±5 were added together; from the summation, a factor needed to get a total of 1000 was derived. This yielded the distribution values of Fig. 3-5(a). Next, each value was placed into a bin of width $y = 0.5$, as shown. The summation of all the values $(16 + 21 + 28, \ldots)$ equals 1000 (except for a rounding-off discrepancy). The result is a crude approximation, but it is adequate for my purpose. Out of the 1000 photons, 75 will head for the $y = 0$ bin, 74 for $y = \pm0.5$, 71 for $y = \pm1$, and so forth. These are reasonable values, and would in fact appear as film exposure if only a single slit is open and the interference mechanism cannot operate.

The procedure used to derive Fig. 3-5(a) was applied to the film exposure display of Fig. 3-3(d), yielding Fig. 3-5(b). Here, out of the 1000 photons, 150 end up in the $y = 0$ bin. This is reasonable if half of the $y = 0.5$ and $y = -0.5$ photons, from Fig. 3-5(a), are captured by the $y = 0$ bin. But what happens to the 71 photons that, according to Fig. 3-5(a), start out headed for $y = 1$? Figure 3-5(b) tells us that only 2 get through. What

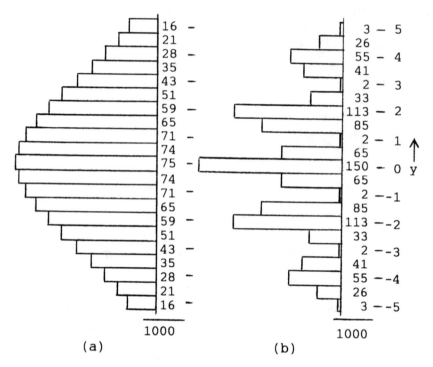

Fig. 3-5.   Photon exposure distributions at the film of Fig. 3-3(a) if bins are
0.5y unit wide: (a)Due to an assumed diffraction attenuation function, $\exp(-0.0625y^2)$, with interference effects omitted. (b)In-
cluding constructive and destructive interference, as in Fig. 3-3(d).

happens to the other 69 photons? They end up in the constructive-interference regions to either side of $y = 1$.

3-5. Individual-Photon Pattern

Finally, instead of 1000 simultaneous photons, we block the light so effectively that *only one isolated photon at a time gets through*—one per second, say. After 1000 seconds (16 2/3 minutes), we develop the film. We
expect to see Fig. 3-5(a) because constructive or destructive interference
could not possibly occur with individual one-at-a-time photons. Instead,
however, *we get Fig. 3-5(b)!*

   This is an unbelievable result, impossible to explain by classical
physics. It defies common sense.

The evidence would have us believe that the photon somehow divides in half, and each half goes through a slit. Upon emerging from the slit, each half is apparently associated with an EMF that is similar to that of 1000 simultaneous photons (except, of course, that the total EMF energy is that of a single photon). The emerging EMFs cover the entire film of Fig. 3-3(a), from $y = -5$ to $+5$. The energy of the EMF that strikes the film should be modified by constructive and destructive interference, as depicted in Fig. 3-3(d). Instead, the photon behaves like a point particle, lands on the film at $y = 4$, say, and *all* of its energy is converted into a single bright dot at $y = 4$. After 1000 seconds, it will turn out that some 55 photons [a value given by Fig. 3-5(b)] were captured by the $y = 4$ bin; 150 landed in the $y = 0$ bin; and so forth.

There are two serious problems with the above recital. First, since a photon is the "irreducible constituent" of an EMF, it cannot split into two halves, each passing through one of the slits. Second, if the photon gives birth to an EMF that covers the entire film from $y = -5$ to $+5$, the photon's energy would reside in this field, leaving much less than a normal amount for the wave packet that eventually strikes and exposes the film at $y = 4$.

These problems have confounded physicists for many years. Much of Nick Herbert's *Quantum Reality* (1985), Jim Baggott's *The Meaning of Quantum Theory* (1992), David Lindley's *Where Does the Weirdness Go?* (1996), and Robert Mills's *Space, Time, and Quanta* (1994) are devoted to various explanations, with various degrees of plausibility. The difficulty is that there is no satisfactory realistic theory, as I have stressed above, based on quantum mechanics or classical physics. Quantum mechanics is inappropriate for describing the behavior of an individual photon or electron. One must conjecture outside the limits of classical or quantum physics.

3-6. The Wave-Particle Duality Field

In what follows, the existence of a field that is analogous to an electromagnetic field is proposed. In the photon model of Fig. 3-6, it is called a wave-particle duality field, or WPD field. As a more palatable example, first consider the duality field of an electron, which is a "particle" but at the same time is associated with a "wave." It usually turns out that the electron's "wave" is an X ray! However, it is an X ray in frequency only. Constructive and destructive interference patterns show that it is some kind of a field; it has a frequency that is determined by the electron's velocity when it strikes the two-slit apparatus. But it is *not* an X-ray field; exposure of the photographic film shows a single sharp point due to the electron, and not an interference pattern due to X rays (which, of course, *are* electromagnetic fields). Similarly, the WPD field of Fig. 3-6 is not an EMF. The drawing immediately suggests what it could be.

My conjecture is that it is a type of compression shock wave generated as the photon plows through the ether (although it is nominally a "compression" wave, it actually consists of compressions and expansions). This is analogous to air versus a high-speed projectile. Air supports the propagation of sound waves, and a projectile forms a shock wave. The shock wave consists of compressions (and expansions) propagating at the speed of sound. Constructive and destructive interference always show up when the shock wave reaches a reflecting object or refractive medium.

Analogously, the ether supports the propagation of EMFs, and the photon "projectile" forms a shock wave that propagates at the speed of the EMF. It would be premature, however, to think that the WPD field really is a shock wave. We know a great deal about air and sound shock waves,

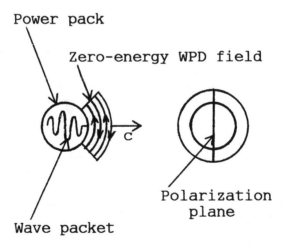

Fig. 3-6. Schematic model of a photon that can account for single, isolated-photon two-slit interference effects. The power pack contains EMF wave packet energy, $E = fh$. It is preceded by a zero-energy wave-particle duality (WPD) field as the photon moves to the right with velocity c. The WPD field may simply be a type of compression shock wave generated as the photon plows through the ether.

but we do not know what the ether or an electric or magnetic field really are. Despite this ignorance, we get through life drawing electric and magnetic field lines, and designing sophisticated equipment based upon imaginary field intensities and flux densities. In the world of imaginary field lines that follows, we assume that the WPD field lines of Fig. 3-6 really exist because they are associated with experimentally revealed constructive and destructive interference.

However, one should not pursue the analogies too far. A sonic boom carries a tremendous amount of energy, but the WPD field may not carry any energy at all. Zero energy? The ether is a peculiar medium: we peer at photons, tiny wave packets that have been traveling for billions of years through the ether *without attenuation*. From another viewpoint, there can be no attenuation because the latter implies the conversion of photon energy into heat, which in turn implies that some particle that has mass (such as an atom) will vibrate more rapidly as it absorbs this energy. But there are no atoms in the ether, or at least none that has absorbed the energy of this billion-year-old wave packet (which is why we can detect it, of course). In other words, the ether is a perfectly elastic, lossless, linear medium; the transverse ripple of Fig. 1-1 is passed along, without change, at the velocity of propagation.

Closer to home, and something about which we know a great deal, there is the zero attenuation of superconductivity and superfluidity:

For many electrical conductors (and, recently, semiconductors), if they are cooled towards 0 K, a transition temperature is reached at which, suddenly, electrical resistance vanishes. Other changes also take place at the transition temperature: magnetic fields are expelled, and thermal properties are altered. The theoretical explanation for superconductivity was presented, in 1957, by J. Bardeen, L. N. Cooper, and J. R. Schrieffer.

Helium liquefies at 4.22 K. If it is further cooled, to 2.172 K, a transition occurs at which, suddenly, viscosity vanishes. The superfluid is able to flow at high speed through tiny holes. Here, also, other changes take place at the transition temperature.

Before the days of superconductivity and superfluidity, we could not conceive of zero electrical resistance and zero viscosity. They were amazing experimental discoveries (superconductivity by H. K. Onnes in 1911). In this same spirit of open-mindedness, we may conjecture that the WPD field can certainly be a zero-energy field if it is not required to do work. From here on, in this book, it is conjectured that the WPD field shock wave consists of compressions (and expansions) of the ether that do not convey any energy.

Is the WPD field a transverse vibration, like the wave packet in the "power pack," or is it a longitudinal vibration, which we expect for a "compression shock wave"? There is evidence that supports either conjecture. The transverse viewpoint is pictured in Fig. 3-6; that of a longitudinal vibration is illustrated at the end of this section.

Figure 3-6 is of course meant to be a schematic representation. Inside the "power pack" is the wave packet of Fig. 1-1, a minuscule EMF whose frequency is the most important specification of the photon, with energy given by $E = fh$. In the side view, the photon is flying off to the right at velocity c. Preceding it is the WPD field. Lines in the so-called compression shock wave have the same spacing as those of the power pack because the frequencies are the same; this is shown to be so by interference patterns. I will not conjecture how all of this can come about.

The WPD field is polarized as depicted in the end view. (Vertical polarization is shown, so this is also the direction of the $\underline{E}$ lines in the power pack.)

The WPD field extends over a cone whose projection, in Fig. 3-6, runs from $+45°$ to $-45°$ relative to the axis of propagation. The $\pm45°$ angle is a matter of convenience, and is much more than is necessary to demonstrate interference in an actual apparatus.

How far does the WPD field extend in front of the power pack? At least 10 or 20 wavelengths, enough to get a reasonably effective degree of destructive interference. The WPD field may therefore be finite, like the strong-force field of Chap. 2. It may be infinite, like an $\underline{E}$ or $\underline{H}$ or graviton field, but this is unlikely because it would violate the "maximum velocity $= c$" rule: If the power pack is moving to the right with velocity c, and the WPD field expands toward infinity with velocity c, then the WPD field would move with velocity $2c$ relative to a stationary reference. Following this line of thought, it is more reasonable to conjecture that the hydrogen electron of Fig. 2-1(b), as it spirals from the $n = 2$ to $n = 1$ orbit, first generates a finite WPD field before it releases the photon's power pack. The electron spiral could be a very gradual multi-revolution locus.

The model of a finite, decaying-exponential WPD field is considered in Section 8 of this chapter. A "photograph" would show a single assembly, as in Fig. 3-6.

Views (a) to (g) of Fig. 3-7 depict how the photon WPD model of Fig. 3-6 can explain the single, isolated-photon two-slit experimental results of Fig. 3-3 (the slits are greatly magnified for the sake of clarity):

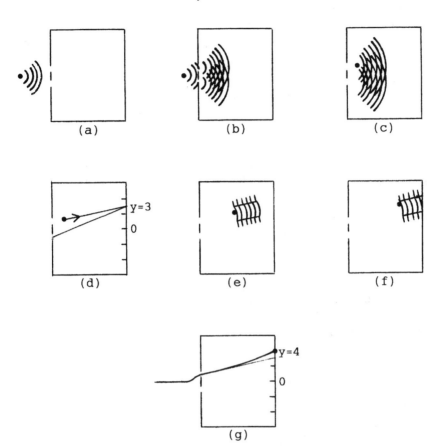

Fig. 3-7.   Sequence that illustrates two-slit interference effects that accompany a single, isolated photon: (a)Photon approaching the slit plate. (b)Leading portion of WPD field has split, with a fragment getting through each of the slits. (c)The WPD fields have progressed beyond the slit plate. The power pack, because of predetermined but statistically random past history, has followed the upper-slit WPD segment. (d)Same as (c), but with WPD fields omitted. The power pack is heading for the $y = 3$ point of the photographic film. (e)The power pack and net WPD field, halfway across. (f)Because WPD field lines are concave, the power pack is directed away from the destructive-interference $y = 3$ point. (g)The power pack locus curves, exposing film at the $y = 4$ point. The ethereal WPD field has vanished without a trace.

In (a), the photon is approaching the two-slit apparatus.

In (b), the leading portion of the WPD field has split, with a fragment getting through each of the slits. The fragments diffract. Thus far, the action is identical to that of a laser beam directed at the two slits.

In (c), we depart from a conventional perspective. The power pack and at least some of the WPD field are inseparable, since it is impossible to generate a shock wave without the power pack. In getting to (c), the photon has three choices: (1)Strike the slit plate at the center, in which event the power-pack's energy is converted into heat, and the WPD field vanishes without a trace; (2)The power pack can pass through the upper slit. This is the choice shown in Fig. 3-7(c); (3)The power pack can pass through the lower slit. The actual path taken by the photon is predetermined but statistically random, based on its prior history.

There is a serious problem here with regard to the lateral movement from (b) to (c). Because the photon has zero mass, one may think it can be pushed sideways without the expenditure of force. This is not so for a photon that, after all, travels at the speed of light. The *effective* mass is given by $E = mc^2$ or, combined with Planck's law, we have

$$\text{Effective mass } (m_{\text{eff}}) = \frac{\text{frequency } (f) \times \text{Planck's constant } (h)}{\text{velocity of light squared } (c^2)}$$

For the photon generated when an electron spirals from the $n = 2$ to $n = 1$ orbit of Fig. 2-1(b), $f = 2.467 \times 10^{15}$ Hz, so the above equation yields $m_{\text{eff}} = 1.819 \times 10^{-35}$ kilogram. This is a truly minuscule mass. It is 50,000 times lighter than an electron. (This should be borne in mind by those who are designing equipment to detect through which of the two slits the photon traveled. An effective photon mass that equals that of an electron is obtained with a frequency of 1.236×10^{20} Hz; this is on the borderline between X and gamma rays.)

The $n = 2$- to 1-orbit photon is more impressive if one calculates momentum:

$$\text{Momentum } (p) = \text{mass } (m) \times \text{velocity } (v).$$

(The eff subscript is omitted because this equation holds for *any* mass.) We get $p = (1.819 \times 10^{-35})(2.998 \times 10^8) = 5.453 \times 10^{-27}$ kilogram · meter/second. The electron in orbit 1 has a momentum of $p = (9.109 \times 10^{-31})(2.188 \times 10^6) = 1.993 \times 10^{-24}$ kg · m/s. Thus, the orbiting electron has "only" 366 times as much momentum as the $n = 2$- to 1-orbit photon.

Nevertheless, despite its minuscule effective mass, a finite force has to act on the photon to achieve lateral deflection. If the two-slit experiment is performed using a laser beam, there is plenty of energy in the EMF to support lateral movement, but not with a single, isolated photon.

Although it may not be valid to think of the photon as being similar to a high-speed projectile in air, the analogy suggests a solution to the lateral-force problem. The conjecture is that the ether forms streamlines through the two slits, and these guide or steer the photon. The ether supplies the lateral force, much as a glancing blow can force a projectile in air to change its course. There is no change in kinetic energy if no change in speed is involved, so the lateral push need not entail a change in energy.

The lateral force is reminiscent of the force of attraction between two conducting, uncharged plates brought sufficiently close together in a high vacuum. The minuscule force is known as the H. B. G. Casimir effect. It may be possible that this force, which has been measured [S. K. Lamoreaux, 1997], is another zero-energy phenomenon.

What are streamlines? In smoothly flowing water (a nonturbulent "stream"), they trace out the flow lines. Think of the ether as flowing through the slits. This implies that the ether is not a passive jelly. The conjecture here is that the ether is a perfectly elastic medium in which streamlines are ubiquitous. The streamlines in an all-pervading ether guide the compression shock waves; this is reminiscent of the pilot wave proposal of David Bohm [D. Bohm and B. Hiley, 1993].

Returning to Fig. 3-7: (d) is the same as (c), except that the WPD fields are omitted for the sake of clarity. We now see that the particular WPD field fragment to which the power pack was attached, in (c), has directed the power pack to $y = 3$.

In (e), the power pack is midway between the two-slit plate and the photographic film. Because it is approaching a destructive-interference point, the WPD field lines are concave, as in Fig. 3-5. This translates into ether stream lines that laterally push or "encourage" the power pack to head for the constructive-interference points at $y = 2$ or 4.

In (f), the power pack is shown on a path toward $y = 4$.

In (g), the power pack arrives at the film, exposing a tiny dot at the $y = 4$ position. According to Fig. 3-5(b), if 1000 individual photons are launched in this way, in sequence, 55 of them will end up in the $y = 4$ slot, and only 2 in the $y = 3$ slot.

Figure 3-7(g) shows the path taken by the power pack. The various curves are explained as the result of lateral forces exerted by the ether upon the photon. The WPD field is an ethereal compression shock wave; it vanishes without a trace.

The concept that the WPD field may be a longitudinal wave is depicted in Fig. 3-8(a). To the right of the power packs, black and white strips symbolize compression and expansion of the ether, respectively. The split paths, in which the power pack proceeds through the upper slit, is illustrated.

In Fig. 3-8(b), the WPD field lines interfere; the ethereal streamlines follow the interference maximum summation peaks. These correspond to regions where the E field intensity is maximum in Fig. 3-4; it is these points that guide the streamlines, which "encourage" the power packs to end up near constructive interference maximum points.

3-7. Interferometer Experiment

This chapter continues with the discussion of an experiment that yields a result that cannot be explained by any existing reality, but which can be explained by the model of Fig. 3-6. This is referred to in Fig. 3-9, which is discussed by Paul Kwiat et al. (1996). Figure 3-9 depicts a "thought experiment" suggested by Avshalom C. Elitzur and Lev Vaidman, but Kwiat and his colleagues have verified the concept in a relatively complicated laboratory setup. Only the much simpler thought experiment will be considered.

In each of the seven parts [(a) to (g)] of Fig. 3-9, a *single,* isolated photon enters at the lower left corner, and strikes a beam splitter. The latter is analogous to an imperfect mirror: About half of the photons that strike the beam splitter will pass through to the right, as in (a) and (b); the other half are subjected to a mirror-type reflection, as in (c) and (d). (One can identify the photon by its "power pack," of course. Although four photons are shown in almost every part, they are the *same* photon "photographed" at different stages of its flight.)

The apparatus of Fig. 3-9 contains a second beam splitter. In (a), the photon, moving upward, strikes the second beam splitter and is reflected to the right. In (b), however, it passes through and continues to move in an upward direction. In (c), the photon, moving to the right, strikes the second beam splitter and passes through, continuing to move to the right. In (d), however, it is reflected in an upward direction.

The entering photon has a 25% probability of following each of the four parts [(a) to (d)] in the left column of Fig. 3-9.

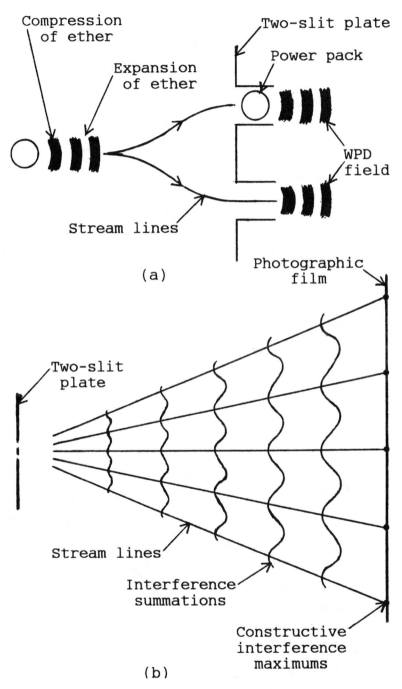

Fig. 3-8. Additional illustration of two-slit plate interference: (a)The WPD
field is depicted as a longitudinal wave. (b)The ethereal streamlines follow the interference maximum summation peaks.

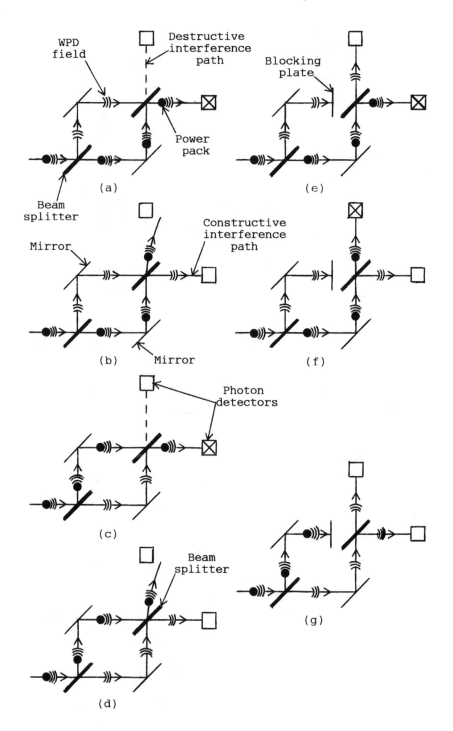

WPD field

Destructive interference path

Blocking plate

Power pack

Beam splitter

(a)

(e)

Mirror

Constructive interference path

(b)

Mirror

(f)

Photon detectors

(c)

Beam splitter

(d)

(g)

The experiment requires two photon detectors, as shown. A photon striking a detector is symbolized by an ✕ in the detector box.

I will now ask you, the reader, to add your own "thought experiment" to the thought experiment: Please erase any paths except those containing three arcs with a power pack (the photons). This is the spirit in which the article by Kwiat et al. is written. However, they imply the presence of wave-particle duality fields (the three arcs without a power pack), without actually admitting that WPD fields exist, because the apparatus is an interferometer. It demonstrates constructive and destructive interference. (You will recognize that it is a variation on the theme represented by the two-slit plate of Fig. 3-3.)

A key element in Fig. 3-9, however, is that the right-hand photon detector is on a constructive interference path, while the upper photon detector is on a destructive interference path, as shown. As Kwiat et al. put it, the "Elitzur–Vaidman experiment gives a photon a choice of two paths to follow. The optical elements are arranged so that photons always go to detector D-light (corresponding to constructive interference) but never to D-dark (corresponding to destructive interference)."

Next, let us conjecture that the model of Fig. 3-6 is correct, that the photon is accompanied by a WPD field. Then the outcome will make sense, and parts (a) to (d) of Fig. 3-9 can be described as follows:

(a): When the entering photon strikes the first beam splitter, it continues to move to the right, preceded by its WPD field. A remnant of the WPD field is reflected upward and then to the right. The power-pack's WPD field, and the "remnant" WPD field, meet at the second beam splitter. They are in-phase at the right-hand detector, generating an ✕. But now a second remnant of the power-pack's WPD field encounters the first remnant on the

---

Fig. 3-9.   Interferometer experiment that yields a strange result [P. Kwiat et al., 1996], but which can be explained by the model of Fig. 3-6. In each part [(a) to (g)], a single, isolated photon enters at the lower left corner. (Although four photons are usually shown, they are the *same* photon "photographed" at different stages of its flight.) The photon is processed by two beam splitters, two mirrors, and two photon detectors. A photon striking a detector is symbolized by an ✕. The entering photon has 25% probability of following each of the scenarios, (a) to (d), in the left column. If a blocking plate is added as shown, (a) becomes (e); (b) becomes (f); (c) and (d) become (g). The strange result is demonstrated by (f): Although the blocking plate does not intercept any photon energy, it is "seen" because the upper detector registers an ✕.

path to the upper detector. These WPD fields are 180° out-of-phase, and cancel each other.

(b): Twenty-five percent of the entering photons will follow the locus depicted in (b). First and second remnants of the power-pack's WPD field are in-phase and reach the right-hand detector; because they are zero-energy compression shock waves "generated as the photon plows through the ether," they vanish without a trace. At the path to the upper detector, however, a minor complication shows up: Because the WPD fields cancel, the power pack, which cannot turn back, veers off to the right (or left) along a *constructive* interference path. Recall that the power pack represents energy, $E = hf$, that cannot simply vanish like a WPD field. It is conjectured that ethereal streamlines guide the power pack to the right (or left) to avoid the destructive-interference (dashed) path.

(c) and (d): The actions at the right-hand and upper photon detectors are a repeat of those of (a) and (b), respectively.

Now, here comes the important and interesting change: A blocking plate is added as shown, interrupting the upper path between a mirror and the second beam splitter. (Kwiat et al. use an exploding pebble rather than a plate, perhaps to add excitement to a recitation that may otherwise be dull, but I am less imaginative.) In Fig. 3-9, with the plate, (a) becomes (e); (b) becomes (f); (c) and (d) both become (g). This is discussed as follows:

(e): The remnant of the entering photon's WPD field is absorbed by the blocking plate. The photon reaches the right-hand detector, generating an ✕. Its second WPD field remnant travels to the upper detector, where it vanishes without a trace.

(f): The remnant of the entering photon's WPD field is absorbed by the blocking plate. The photon reaches the upper detector, generating an ✕. Its second WPD field remnant travels to the right-hand detector, where it vanishes without a trace.

This seemingly unremarkable (f) description is the raison d'etre for the Kwiat et al. article. If you erase (mentally, I trust) the WPD fields in (b) and (f), this is what is left: In (b), a photon enters but is unrecorded. In (f), the blocking plate intercepts nothing at all, but the upper detector reveals the presence of a blocking plate by registering the arrival of a photon. The title of the article, "Quantum Seeing in the Dark," reflects the fact that the apparatus *somehow* "sees" the blocking plate even though no photon (that is, light) is actually intercepted by the blocking plate. The conjectured depiction of Fig. 3-9 says that the plate *does* block something, but it is a WPD field and not the photon that generated the field.

With the blocking plate, 25% of the entering photons follow the (f) scenario, registering $\times$ in the upper detector. (The actual measurements have to be corrected for detector inefficiency).

(g): Fifty percent of the entering photons are absorbed by the blocking plate and, therefore, do not reach a detector. Nevertheless, it is conjectured that WPD fields *do* reach the detectors, that they are compression shock waves in the ether, and they are zero-energy fields that vanish without a trace.

The above analysis solves the "quantum seeing in the dark" mystery. The ether has been resuscitated!

3-8. Decaying-Exponential WPD Field

The chapter is ended with a more detailed consideration of the photon's wave-particle duality field, assuming that it is a decaying "exponential," as depicted in Fig. 3-10(a). This is strictly a viewpoint taken from classical physics. The shape of the field and its spectrum should be independent of frequency, so convenient scales can be chosen. In the equation for the amplitude of the field, y, given in Fig. 3-10(a), the angle is $2\pi x$ or, in degrees, $360x°$. This corresponds to a spatial frequency of 1 cycle/meter, as shown by the x-axis scale. The exponent, $-0.1x$, corresponds to a length constant of 10 cycles; that is, at $x = 10$, the amplitude envelope is $\varepsilon^{-1} = 0.368$ relative to its value at $x = 0$. This is accompanied by a reasonably high quality factor, Q, in the spectrum in Fig. 3-10(b).

Figure 3-10(a) shows a *spatial* waveform rather than a time waveform. The time waveform is seen by a stationary observer as the photon flies by. It is Fig. 3-10(a) reversed; that is, a rising exponential. It is a matter of convenience as to which waveform is used. In the time domain we have a function of t, in second units, and the spectral frequency is $\omega = 2\pi f$, where f has the units of cycles/second; in the spatial waveform discussion, below, we have a function of x in meter units, and the spectral frequency is $\omega = 2\pi f$, where f has the units of cycles/meter.

The idea in Fig. 3-10 is that the WPD field has to be a good sine wave in order to get good destructive interference in the two-slit experiment.

The magnitude of the spectrum of Fig. 3-10(a) is plotted in Fig. 3-10(b), with $f = \omega/2\pi$. This is a spatial frequency spectrum in cycles/meter rather than cycles/second. All important is the quality factor, or Q. The -3 dB (0.707 peak) level in Fig. 3-10(b) extends from $f = 0.9838$ to 1.0157, so $Q = 1/0.0319 = 31$. This is a reasonably high value.

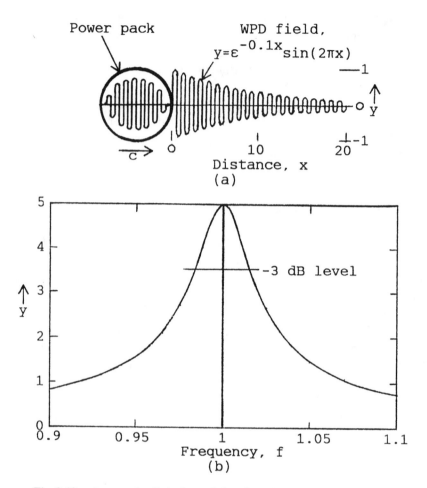

Fig. 3-10. A more detailed view of the photon's WPD field, assuming that it is a decaying exponential: (a)Power pack and WPD field moving to the right with velocity c. The spatial frequency is 1 cycle/meter. (b)Spatial frequency spectrum of the WPD field, in cycles/meter. The Q is 31.

There are indications that the Q does not remain constant. According to Raymond Y. Chiao et al. (1993), the photon wave packet (the power pack in Fig. 3-6) becomes shorter if it passes through a transparent barrier, such as glass, that slows it down. Upon emerging from the barrier, the speed returns to normal (c in vacuum or air), but the shorter wave packet can be interpreted as a steeper exponential decay. This may correspond to increased bandwidth and lower Q in the putative WPD field.

Chapter 4

The Electron Model

4-1. Relativistic Changes

Another sensational experiment that strains quantum reality is one that involves electrons. Because of experimental difficulties, however, this was not successfully demonstrated until 1989 (A. Tonomura et al.). One of the problems is that objects that have mass, such as electrons, become heavier (and shorter) as their velocity increases. Increases, that is, relative to the stationary, nonaccelerating observer who is making the measurements. Therefore, the changes in effective mass and length due to relative velocity are called *relativistic*.

The relativistic change in length (the Lorentz contraction) is considered in Chap. 7, Section 7-2, and is not pertinent to the discussion in the present chapter. Only the relative change in mass is considered.

There are three elementary particles that have mass—the electron, proton, and neutron. As given in Table 1-2, their masses are, respectively, 9.1094×10^{-31}, 1.67262×10^{-27}, and 1.67493×10^{-27} kilogram. Although the present chapter is concerned with objects that have mass, for convenience only the electron rather than proton or neutron is considered. Much of the discussion and conclusions, however, also apply to the proton and neutron.

"Massive" particles display gravitational attraction toward each other. However, as pointed out in Chap. 1 in connection with Newton's universal law of gravitation, this force is relatively weak. It is not pertinent to the present chapter.

If massive particles interact, momentum (p) is conserved. Momentum is given, in Chap. 3, as

$$p = mv,$$

where m is mass and v is velocity. If we add up all of the mv values of the particles *before* they interact, the sum has to equal the sum of mv values *after* they interact. If it is a three-dimensional interaction, one must separately conserve momentum in the x, y, and z directions.

It is interesting to contrast this with the "massless" photon: Photons ignore each other, and two photons that hit each other head-on only yield the algebraic sum of their respective wave packets. Following the "collision," they continue to propagate, unchanged, at the speed of light.

It is sometimes convenient, in this chapter, to consider the effective mass and momentum of a photon: Effective mass is given in Chap. 3 as

$$m_{\text{eff}} = \frac{fh}{c^2}.$$

As one should expect, effective momentum is equal to effective mass times velocity. We get for a photon

$$\text{Effective momentum } (p_{\text{eff}}) = \frac{\text{frequency } (f) \times \text{Planck's constant } (h)}{\text{velocity of light } (c)}.$$

In connection with the photon generated when an electron spirals from the $n = 2$ to $n = 1$ orbit of Fig. 2-1(b): This is a typical photon. In Chap. 3 the following values are calculated: $m_{\text{eff}} = 1.819 \times 10^{-35}$ kilogram and $p_{\text{eff}} = 5.453 \times 10^{-27}$ kilogram · meter/second. These are extremely small values. The m_{eff} is 50,000 times lighter than an electron, while p_{eff} is 366 times smaller than that of the electron in orbit 1 of Fig. 2-1(a). We can immediately conclude, therefore, that even the lightest of "massive" particles, the electron, is a giant compared to a typical photon.

As luck would have it, we are surrounded by inexpensive equipment for examining electrons, in the form of the cathode-ray tube, or television picture tube. A simplified model, without deflection plates or coils, is depicted in Fig. 4-1. In response to a positive voltage V, electrons are accelerated toward the fluorescent screen, striking it at high speed. Some of the electrons' kinetic energy is converted into light (photons). A permanent record of electron strikes can be obtained by placing a photographic film next to the fluorescent screen, as shown.

The potential energy of the electric field is converted into kinetic energy as the electron speeds up. Using a "conventional" equation for the conversion, one finds that the speed of the electron is greater than the speed of light if V is greater than 256,000 volts. This is, of course, impossible. Nothing, and certainly not a material object such as an electron, can travel faster than 3×10^8 meters/second.

What is wrong? The "conventional" equation is at fault. As any material object increases in speed, its *effective mass* increases. The increase is such that, in converting from potential to kinetic energy, the velocity of the object can never reach the speed of light.

The symbol γ is used for the increase-in-mass ratio. For an electron,

$$m_{\text{eff}} = \gamma m_0,$$

where m_0 is the electron's rest mass, 9.1094×10^{-31} kilogram. The electron *behaves* as if it has a mass γm_0 if it is moving, whether this is due to V of a cathode-ray tube or for any other reason.

Some of the numerical values that illustrate the above concepts are given in Table 4-1. The first column lists various voltages, V, applied to the cathode-ray tube anode with respect to its cathode. The second column lists

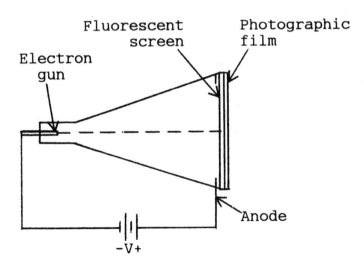

Fig. 4-1. Simplified model, without deflection plates or coils, of a cathode-ray tube. The photographic film provides a permanent record of electron strikes against the fluorescent screen.

the corresponding γ. The third and fourth columns list v/c ratios for the velocity with which an electron strikes the fluorescent screen. Column 3 gives the v/c calculation using the "conventional" equation; column 4 using the correct, relativistic equation. Column 5 gives the correct, relativistic velocity. At relatively low voltages, the conventional and relativistic velocities are approximately the same. Above $V = 25,000$ volts, however, one should only use the relativistic values.

Incidentally, $V = 25,000$ volts is typical for a cathode-ray tube (but the current is very small). Notice that the electron reaches a very impressive velocity, 0.9049×10^8 m/s (56,000 miles/second). No wonder the fluorescent screen lights up!

An important level of V occurs at 510,990 volts, which corresponds to $\gamma = 2$. This value of V is the basis for a convenient unit of electron mass because 510,990 electron volts/$c^2 = m_0$.

A photon behaves as if it has an effective mass and effective momentum. In this way the photon, which is an electromagnetic wave packet, displays the characteristics of a particle that has mass. In 1924, Louis de Broglie (1892–1987) proposed that the reverse may be true—that an electron, which has mass, can display the characteristics of a wave. Soon afterwards, experiments showed that de Broglie's hypothesis was correct; in fact, every mass in motion, in general, demonstrates wave characteristics. De Broglie's conjecture was an important milestone that was recognized by a Nobel prize in 1929; besides, because it was made via a relatively short Ph.D. thesis, it has fired the imagination, if not inspiration, of every Ph.D. physics student since 1924.

The reason for considering the massive electron versus the wavelike photon is that each of them displays an interference pattern in the two-slit apparatus. They are, however, two different species: The electron's field travels at the speed of the electron, which can be anything from zero up to the upper limit, the speed of light, while the photon's WPD field *always* travels at the speed of light. Also, the frequency of the electron's field is a function of its velocity, while the photon's WPD field frequency is that of its power pack. Therefore, in what follows, the electron's field is called a particle-wave duality (PWD) field to distinguish it from the photon's WPD field.

The particle-wave duality (PWD) frequency of an electron is given by the photon's $m_{eff} = fh/c^2$ if we substitute the electron's velocity v in place of the photon's velocity c. This yields

$$\text{Frequency } (f) = \frac{\text{effective mass } (m_{eff}) \times \text{velocity squared } (v^2)}{\text{Planck's constant } (h)}$$

Table 4-1.   Various values associated with an electron as potential energy eV is converted into kinetic energy K. γ is the relativistic increase in mass factor; "v/c conventional" neglects relativistic effects; f_{PWD} and λ_{PWD} are frequency and wavelength of the particle-wave duality field. Because this is *not* an electromagnetic field, the last column is for identification only; no orange, ultraviolet, x-ray, or gamma-ray energy is actually available.

		v/c	
V, volts	γ	Conventional	Relativistic
1	1.000	0.00198	0.00198
10	1.000	0.00626	0.00626
100	1.000	0.01978	0.01978
1000	1.002	0.06256	0.06247
10000	1.020	0.1978	0.1950
25000	1.049	0.3128	0.3018
50000	1.098		0.4127
100000	1.196		0.5482
510990	2		0.8660
10^6	2.957		0.9411
10^7	20.57		0.9988
10^8	196.7		1.0000

V, volts	$v \times 10^8$, m/s	f_{PWD}, Hz	λ_{PWD} angstrom	ID
1	0.00593	4.836×10^{14}	12.26	Orange
10	0.01876	4.836×10^{15}	3.878	Ultraviolet
100	0.05930	4.836×10^{16}	1.226	Ultraviolet
1000	0.1873	4.831×10^{17}	0.3876	X-ray
10000	0.5846	4.790×10^{18}	0.1220	X-ray
25000	0.9049	1.181×10^{19}	0.07664	X-ray
50000	1.237	2.310×10^{19}	0.05355	X-ray
100000	1.644	4.440×10^{19}	0.03701	X-ray
510990	2.596	1.853×10^{20}	0.01401	γ-ray
10^6	2.821	3.236×10^{20}	0.008719	γ-ray
10^7	2.994	2.536×10^{21}	0.001181	γ-ray
10^8	2.998	2.430×10^{22}	0.000123	γ-ray

where $h = 6.6261 \times 10^{-34}$ joule $\cdot$ second. However, since the electron's effective mass is a function of velocity, it is more convenient to substitute $m_{eff} = \gamma m_0$ to get

$$f = \frac{\gamma m_0 v^2}{h}$$

This is the equation used to calculate values in the frequency column, f_{PWD}, of Table 4-1. Wavelength, γ_{PWD}, is given by velocity/frequency, as usual.

4-2. Two-Slit Interference Pattern

The frequency values in Table 4-1 are relatively high. As mentioned above, an electron is a giant compared to a photon, and this shows up in the associated frequency values. At a typical cathode-ray tube value of $V = 25,000$ volts, Table 4-1 shows $f = 1.181 \times 10^{19}$ Hz. According to Table 1-1, this is an X-ray frequency, as is also indicated in the last column of Table 4-1. I hasten to add that these are *not* the X rays that, it is frequently claimed, are emitted by a cathode-ray tube. The electron's particle-wave dual is an X ray in frequency only; it is not an electromagnetic wave; it propagates at the velocity of the electron, not that of light; it has zero energy, zero penetrating power, and vanishes without a trace when the electron strikes its fluorescent screen. Is it realistic for us to believe that it has zero energy? The arguments regarding energy of the photon's zero-energy WPD field apply equally well to the electron's PWD field.

The bona fide X rays that the screen *does* emit are due to the great velocity with which an electron arrives at the screen. Part of the kinetic energy is converted into fluorescent excitation, part into photons in the X-ray range of frequencies, and part into heat. In the case of a television receiver, it is generally considered that the X-ray effect is negligibly small, especially compared to that of deadly program material.

Nevertheless, the high PWD frequencies offer almost insurmountable experimental difficulties in the attempt to demonstrate the incontestable signature of a wave—constructive and destructive interference in the two-slit apparatus. It is interesting to consider, below, how some of the difficulties were overcome.

The proof that an electron can act as a wave came from the same techniques that are used to prove that an X ray is a wave. For example, the above-mentioned $V = 25,000$-volt PWD frequency has a wavelength of

0.077 angstrom (Å). In Fig. 3-3, the spacing between the two slits is around 5 wavelengths, so a spacing of 0.4 Å would be reasonable for the electron beam. The "slits" in this case can be provided—many of them—by the repetitive spacing between the atoms of a crystalline material. Clinton Davisson and Lester Germer, in 1925, showed electron diffraction and interference using a crystal made out of nickel.

In 1989 the "impossible" was accomplished—five physicists (A. Tonomura et al.) used skill, persistence, ingenuity, and modern equipment to demonstrate the particle-wave duality of electrons. In what follows, I am going to take advantage of the accomplishment of Tonomura et al. by using the two-slit photon interference drawings of Chap. 3 and applying them to two-slit electron interference in Chap. 4. Changes in text and drawings of Chap. 3 are made, as needed, to accommodate electrons rather than photons.

As an electron source, Tonomura et al. used a sharp field-emission tip and an anode potential of 50,000 volts. According to Table 4-1, f and λ were 2.3×10^{19} Hz and 0.054 Å. From Tonomura et al.: "When a 50-kV electron hits the fluorescent film, approximately 500 photons are produced from the spot." They used a much more sophisticated light-gathering arrangement, including a magnification of 2000, than the photographic film shown in Fig. 4-1.

For electrons, one must employ a high vacuum, in addition to facing the problems associated with angstrom-size wavelengths. As a vehicle for this discussion, consider the idealized two-slit interference-diffraction apparatus of Fig. 4-2(a). The electron beam is moving to the right. It strikes a plate that contains two slits. Some of the electrons get through the upper slit, and some through the lower slit. To the right of the slits, the electrons spread out, via diffraction, as if they had wave characteristics. Two of the rays thus formed, (1) of length ℓ_1 and (2) of length ℓ_2, are shown as they come together on a fluorescent screen. A relatively high voltage is used so that the electrons will have sufficient energy to elicit a fluorescent response that can be recorded on the film. What pattern will the exposed film show?

In some locations, the PWD field from ray (1) is in-phase with that of ray (2) when they meet at the screen, and the electrons associated with the PWD fields increase film exposure (constructive interference). At other locations, the PWD fields have opposite phases, and the electrons avoid these regions (destructive interference). Figure 4-2(b) illustrates an in-between situation in which the PWD fields are 90° out-of-phase. The net results of constructive and destructive interference are the idealized set of peaks and valleys of Fig. 4-2(c).

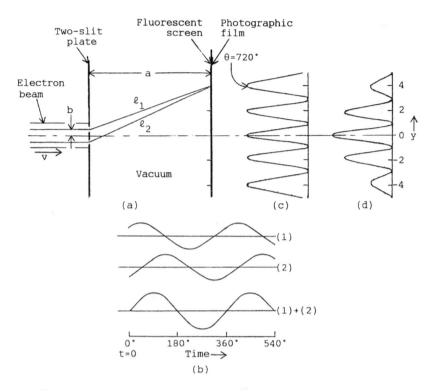

Fig. 4-2. Two-slit interference and diffraction: (a)Schematic of idealized apparatus based on the fact that Tonomura et al. have demonstrated the particle-wave duality (PWD) of electrons. The slits are at right angles to the page. Two of the semi-infinite number of rays leaving the slits are depicted as they meet at $y = 4$ of the fluorescent screen. (b)Waveforms of rays (1) and (2) when they meet at the screen if they are 90° out of phase. (c)Idealized screen-film pattern. (d)The screen-film pattern is "corrected" by adding the attenuation that accompanies diffraction.

Figure 4-2(a) and (c) depict the following relative values:

$$b = 0.5, a = 10, y = 4,$$

and $\theta = 720° = 4\pi$ (it is the second peak away from the $y = 0$ axis). The numerical values correspond to PWD field relative wavelength $\lambda = 0.1857$. Ray ℓ_2 is 10.97 units long and contains 59 cycles of PWD field. Ray ℓ_1 is 10.59 units long and contains 57 cycles. Therefore, the two signals arrive in phase (constructive interference).

At $y = 1$, $\theta \cong 180° = \pi$, the longer path is 54.4 cycles long, the shorter path is 53.9 cycles long, so the difference is 0.5 cycle. Therefore, the two signals cancel (destructive interference).

A change has been applied to Fig. 4-2(c) to convert it into the more realistic film exposure of Fig. 4-2(d). Since diffraction is accompanied by attenuation, Fig. 4-2(c) has been multiplied by $\exp(-0.0625y^2)$ to get Fig. 4-2(d).

Now consider that the electron beam carries kinetic energy. If an electron does not arrive at the screen because of destructive interference, it must be picked up by regions of constructive interference. How this can happen is crudely shown in Fig. 4-3. We now have three parallel PWD fields propagating to the right: upper, middle, and lower. The numerical values give putative electric field intensities if the PWD fields are analogous to electromagnetic fields; although they are *not* EMFs, but behave like EMFs, I speculate that I can use the analogy.

After each electron gets past the double slits, it diffracts by an amount that is based on its predetermined but statistically random prior

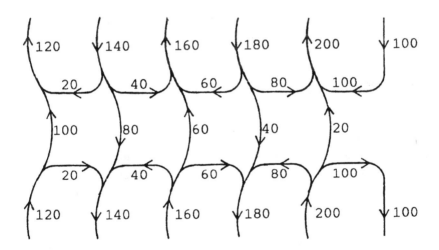

Propagation ⟶

Fig. 4-3. Crude depiction of three parallel PWD fields propagating to the right, with destructive interference in the middle path, but with constructive interference in the upper and lower paths. The numerical values give putative electric field intensities if the PWD fields are analogous to EMFs. Because of the interaction between concave and convex lines, electrons are directed toward regions of constructive interference.

experiences. Then, because of the bending of the pseudo-$\underline{E}$ lines in Fig. 4-3, entering electrons veer off toward the upper and lower paths, avoiding the middle destructive-interference path. In other words, in Fig. 4-2(a), the electrons actually curve away from destructive-interference points $y = \pm 1$ and ± 3, and toward constructive-interference points $y = 0, \pm 2,$ and ± 4. As a result of this "curving away," the valleys of Fig. 4-2(c) and (d) are created.

4-3. Simultaneous-Burst Pattern

Our next step is to carefully decrease the output of the electron beam. Suppose that an ideally fast pulse allows a burst of only 1000 electrons to *simultaneously* fly through the slits. The procedure used to derive Fig. 3-5(b), for a photon beam, was applied to the film exposure display of Fig. 4-2(d), yielding Fig. 4-4(b). Here, out of the 1000 electrons, 150 end up in the $y = 0$ bin. This is reasonable if half of the $y = 0.5$ and $y = -0.5$ electrons, from Fig. 4-4(a), are captured by the $y = 0$ bin. But what happens to the 71 electrons that, according to Fig. 4-4(a), start out headed for $y = 1$? Figure 4-4(b) tells us that only 2 get through. What happens to the other 69 electrons? They end up in the constructive-interference regions to either side of $y = 1$.

4-4. Individual-Electron Pattern

Finally, instead of 1000 simultaneous electrons, we restrict the beam so effectively that *only one isolated electron at a time gets through*—one per second, say. After 1000 seconds, we develop the film. We expect to see Fig. 4-4(a) because constructive or destructive interference could not possibly occur with individual electrons. Instead, we get Fig. 4-4(b)! This is an unbelievable result, impossible to explain by classical physics or realistic quantum physics.

The Tonomura et al. paper is titled "Demonstration of Single-Electron Buildup of an Interference Pattern." In its entirety their abstract follows:

The wave-particle duality of electrons was demonstrated in a kind of two-slit interference experiment using an electron microscope equipped with an electron biprism and a position-sensitive electron-counting system. Such an experiment has been regarded as a pure thought experiment that can never be realized. This article reports an experiment that successfully recorded the actual buildup process of the interference pattern with a series of incoming single electrons in the form of a movie.

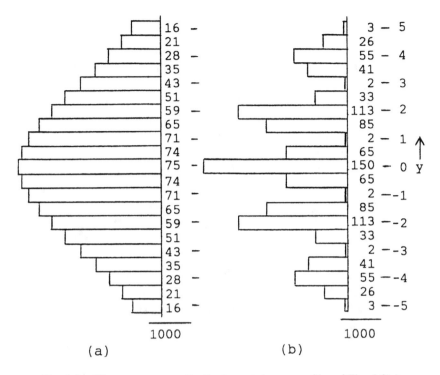

Fig. 4-4.   Electron exposure distributions at the screen-film of Fig. 4-2(a) if bins are 0.5y unit wide. (a)Due to an assumed diffraction attenuation function, $\exp(-0.0625y^2)$, with interference effects omitted. (b)Including constructive and destructive interference, as in Fig. 4-2(d).

The Tonomura et al. experiments show that the film exposure display of Fig. 4-2(d) occurs independent of electron beam density. Their paper reproduces five film exposures showing how the electron interference pattern builds up as the number of *individual* electrons striking the fluorescent screen increases as follows: 10, 100, 3000, 20,000, and 70,000. In my opinion, this illustration is one of the most remarkable in the history of science.

The evidence would have us believe that an electron somehow divides in half, and each half goes through a slit. Upon emerging from the slit, each half is apparently associated with an EMF that is similar to that of 1000 simultaneous electrons (except that the total EMF energy is that of a single electron). The emerging EMFs cover the entire screen of Fig. 4-2(a), from $y = -5$ to $+5$. The energy of the EMF that strikes the screen should be modified by constructive and destructive interference, as depicted in

Fig. 4-2(d). Instead, the electron behaves like a point particle, lands on the screen at $y = 4$, say, and *all* of its energy is converted into a single bright dot at $y = 4$. After 1000 seconds, it will turn out that some 55 electrons [a value given by Fig. 4-4(b)] were captured by the $y = 4$ bin; 150 landed in the $y = 0$ bin; and so forth.

There are two serious problems with the above recital. First, since an electron is an irreducible constituent of matter, it cannot split into two halves, each passing through one of the slits. Second, if the electron gives birth to an EMF-type field that covers the entire screen from $y = -5$ to $+5$, the electron's energy would reside in this field, leaving less than a normal amount for the particle that eventually strikes and stimulates fluorescence at $y = 4$.

4-5. The Particle-Wave Duality Field

In what follows, I propose that the electron is accompanied by a PWD field, depicted in Fig. 4-5, that is similar to the photon's WPD field of Fig. 3-6. "Similar," but different in two major respects: (1)The electron and its entourage can move at any velocity *less than c*, whereas a photon propagates *at* velocity c (through a vacuum); (2)the frequency of the electron's PWD field is a function of v, given by $f = \gamma m_0 v^2/h$, whereas the frequency of the photon's field is equal to that of its power pack (the wave packet). Because of these differences, it is necessary to classify the two fields as belonging to altogether different species.

My conjecture here is that the electron's PWD field is a type of compression *wind* generated as the electron flies through the ether (although it is nominally a "compression" wind, it actually consists of compressions and expansions). This is analogous to air versus a low-speed projectile, such as a pitched baseball. In the ether, the PWD field of Fig. 4-5 corresponds to compressions and expansions that precede the power pack. It is again conjectured that these ethereal waves do not convey any energy.

My argument regarding zero energy paraphrases the discussion in Chap. 3. There is no attenuation of electrons in a vacuum provided we restrict it to a special case—the vacuum must not contain $\underline{E}$ or $\underline{H}$ fields, since the electron may interact (accelerate or decelerate) with these fields. In the absence of $\underline{E}$ or $\underline{H}$ fields, an electron travels in a straight line, at constant speed, in a vacuum. A change in speed implies the conversion of electron energy into heat, which in turn implies that some particle, such as an atom, will vibrate more rapidly as it absorbs this energy. But there are of course no atoms in our vacuum; it consists of ether and nothing else, so the PWD fields

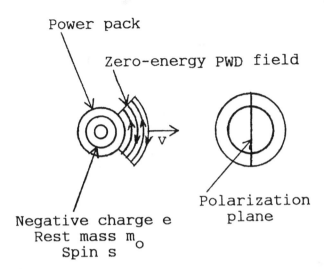

Fig. 4-5. Schematic model of an electron that can account for single, isolated-electron two-slit interference effects. The power pack represents charge, rest mass, and spin. It is preceded by a zero-energy PWD field as the electron moves to the right with velocity v. The PWD field may simply be a type of compression wind generated as the electron flies through the ether.

have to be zero-energy fields. The ether, if it exists, is a perfectly elastic, lossless, linear medium.

Figure 4-5 is meant to be a schematic representation. Inside the "power pack" is a negative charge, $e = 1.6022 \times 10^{-19}$ coulomb, mass $m_0 = 9.1094 \times 10^{-31}$ kilogram, and normalized spin $s = \frac{1}{2}$. The spin of a particle is its angular momentum that exists even when the particle is at rest, just as it has a mass m_0 at rest. (Here we *can* think of the particle as if it is a minute spinning baseball. The spin of an electron enters into the discussion in Section 4-6 of this chapter.) In the side view of Fig. 4-5, the electron is flying off to the right at velocity v. Preceding it is the PWD field whose frequency and wavelength are given by $f = \gamma m_0 v^2 / h$ and $\lambda = v/f$.

The picture that emerges is this: An electron at rest has a negative charge e, mass m_0, and spin s. As soon as it starts to move, a PWD field develops. For example, when it has converted 1 volt into kinetic energy, Table 4-1 tells us that the electron model is moving (to the right, say) at a velocity of 593,000 meters/second (1,326,000 miles/hour). This is relatively slow for an electron! The PWD field lines are 6 angstroms apart between $+$ and $-$ (the wavelength is 12 Å). The lines zoom by at a frequency of 4.836×10^{14} Hz. Although this corresponds to an orange glow, there is of course no visible effect when the electron strikes the two-slit plate. The PWD field, to repeat, is not an EMF, and probably carries zero energy.

As an electron accelerates, frequency increases and the wavelength shrinks. At 25,000 volts, $f = 1.18 \times 10^{19}$ hertz and $\lambda = 0.077$ angstrom. Beyond this, relativistic effects become appreciable; the electron behaves as if its mass is increasing in accordance with γm_0. At a potential of 510,990 volts, $\gamma = 2$, the PWD frequency is 1.85×10^{20} Hz, and $\lambda = 0.014$ Å.

The experiment of Tonomura et al. shows that the PWD really exists. It may not look like the wave peaks depicted in Fig. 4-5, but the electron interference pattern is there, literally in black and white. Their pattern agrees with the 50,000-volt calculated wavelength of 0.054 angstrom. At this voltage, relativistic effects are also verified since γ is appreciably greater than 1 (it is 1.10).

Is the PWD field longitudinal, like a sound wave, or transverse? For a photon, polarization shows that the WPD field is transverse. In "copycat" fashion, therefore, I show the electron's PWD field as having a polarization plane in Fig. 4-5, but this is conjecture. If the field is a compression wind wave in the ether, however, it is analogous to a longitudinal wind disturbance in air, and the polarization plane becomes meaningless.

The changes in effective mass and PWD wavelength occur because the electron is moving—with respect to what? With respect to the electron gun in a cathode-ray tube in a physics laboratory? Why should movement induce the mass change? What about the relativistic effect: Are we prepared to say that an observer moving with the electron (as it drifts at constant speed past the anode, say), will see no change in mass and no PWD field? It seems to me that it is much easier to visualize these changes if an ether is present. As the electron flies through the ether, a "viscosity" interaction induces wind waves (the PWD field) and also resists high particle speed via an effective increase in mass. The latter could simply be due to the effective mass of the ether that is carried along by the power pack.

So a photon can travel through the ether at the speed of light, without attenuation, whereas an electron runs up against an ether that has effective mass. These are, indeed, strange conjectures.

How far does the PWD field extend in front of the power pack? At least 10 or 20 wavelengths, enough to get a reasonably effective degree of destructive interference. The model of a finite, decaying-exponential PWD field is considered in Section 4-7 of this chapter. A "photograph" would show a single assembly, as in Fig. 4-5.

Views (a) to (g) of Fig. 4-6 now depict how the electron model of Fig. 4-5 can explain the single, isolated-electron two-slit experimental results of Fig. 4-2. The text would follow almost word-for-word the photon discus-

sion of Chap. 3 in connection with Fig. 3-7. The caption of Fig. 4-6 is sufficiently detailed to serve as the text with a minimum of further explanation.

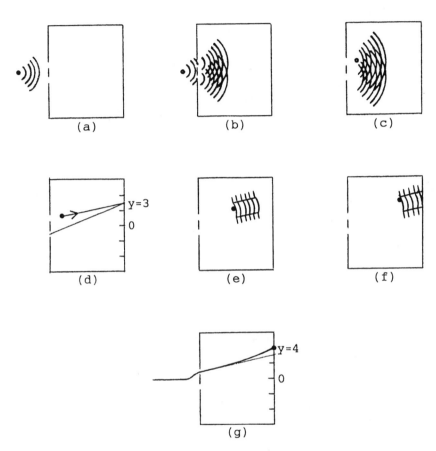

Fig. 4-6. Sequence that illustrates two-slit interference effects that accompany a single, isolated electron. (a)Electron approaching the slit
plate. (b)Leading portion of PWD field has split, with a fragment
getting through each of the slits. (c)The PWD fields have progressed beyond the slit plate. The power pack, because of predetermined but statistically random past history, has followed the
upper-slit PWD segment. (d)Same as (c), but with PWD fields
omitted. The power pack is heading for the $y = 3$ point of the
screen-film. (e)The power pack and net PWD field, halfway
across. (f)Because PWD field lines are concave, the power pack is
directed away from the destructive-interference $y = 3$ point.
(g)The power pack locus curves, striking the screen-film at the
$y = 4$ point. The ethereal PWD field has vanished without a trace.

With regard to the lateral force needed to change the electron's direction in going from Fig. 4-6(b) to (c), it is again conjectured that the ether forms streamlines through the two slits. These guide or steer the electron as the ether supplies the lateral force that is required. There is no change in kinetic energy if no change in speed is involved, so the lateral push need not entail a change in energy.

In Fig. 4-6(e), the power pack is midway between the two-slit plate and the fluorescent screen. Because it is approaching a destructive-interference point, the PWD field lines are concave, as in Fig. 4-3. This "encourages" the power pack to head for the constructive-interference points at $y = 2$ or 4.

Figure 4-6(g) shows the path taken by the power pack. The PWD field is an ethereal compression wind; it vanishes without a trace.

Tonomura et al. do not attempt to explain the unrealistic experimental outcome. The statistical predictions of quantum mechanics are of no help here because we are dealing with the interference pattern associated with a *single* electron.

4-6. Electron-Spin Experiment

This chapter continues with consideration of an experimental setup that yields a result that cannot be explained by any existing reality, but which can be explained by the model of Fig. 4-5. I am referring to Fig. 4-7, which is discussed by David Z. Albert (1994).

We have two identical devices that measure electron spin; they are represented by triangles. The spin-measuring function is not important here; instead, observe that the triangles cause a 90° change in spin direction. If a right-spinning (R) electron enters the first triangle, it comes out either as an up-spinning (U) or down-spinning (D) electron. If a U or D electron enters the second triangle, it comes out either as an R electron or as a left-spinning (L) electron.

All of the electrons fed into the equipment have preselected R spins, but 50% develop U spins and the other 50% develop D spins. They enter individually, one at a time.

Figure 4-7(a) illustrates the scenario of the 50% that develop U spins. When an R electron enters the first triangle, its PWD field splits, half taking the up path and, simultaneously of course, half taking the down path. The power pack, based upon its past history, takes the U path. Both paths are brought together with the aid of reflectors (not shown), which, say, cause the electron loci to again become horizontal. When the U electron

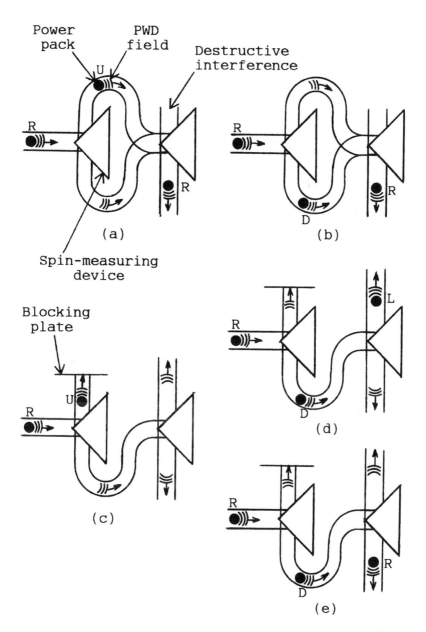

Fig. 4-7. Experiment that yields strange results [D. Z. Albert, 1994], but which can be explained by the model of Fig. 4-5. R, L, U, and D are right-spinning, left-spinning, up-spinning, and down-spinning electrons, respectively. Each spin-measuring device causes a 90° change in spin direction. All of the input electrons have preselected R spins, but 50% develop U spins and the other 50% develop D spins. (a)If an entering electron develops a U spin. (b)If entering electron develops a D spin. In (c), (d), and (e), the U output of the first spin-measuring device is blocked by a plate. (c)Same as (a) with block. (d)Same as (b) with block, but D electron develops an L spin. (e)Same as (b) with block, but D electron develops an R spin.

enters the second triangle, a strange effect results: only R electrons leave the triangle. Apparently, the phase relationships are such that destructive interference between the upper and lower PWD field branches occurs, so that there is no L output. Instead, with the aid of constructive interference, all of the power packs emerge as R electrons.

Figure 4-7(b) illustrates the scenario of the 50% that develop D spins. As before, when an R electron enters the first triangle, its PWD fields split. This time the power pack, based upon its past history, takes the D path. When this D electron enters the second triangle, only R electrons again leave the triangle. Apparently, the phase relationships are such that destructive interference between the upper and lower PWD field branches again occurs, so that there is no L output.

Figure 4-7(c), (d), and (e) depict the outcomes if a blocking plate is placed over the U output of the first triangle. Figure 4-7(c), like (a), illustrates the scenario of the 50% that develop U spins. These power packs strike the blocking plate, where their kinetic energy is converted into heat. The lower PWD field splits, and the two segments leave the second triangle as shown. These are zero-energy fields that vanish.

Figure 4-7(d), like (b), illustrates the scenario of the 50% that develop D spins. Now, because of the blocking plate, another strange effect results: with only one PWD field, interference cannot take place. Now there *is* an L output, as shown. This is the path taken by half of the D electrons that enter the second triangle; the other half take the R output path, as shown in Fig. 4-7(e).

To summarize: *Without* the blocking plate, 100% of the entering electrons leave as R electrons. *With* the blocking plate, 50% are absorbed by the plate, 25% leave as R electrons, but 25% leave as L electrons. It is explained by constructive and destructive interference as the zero-energy PWD fields interact. Remember, however, the basic conjectures: that the PWD fields are compression (nominally) wind waves in the ether, and the electrons tend to be guided by streamlines in the ether, which can also supply lateral forces.

Again, the particle-wave duality field model solves the mystery, and puts in evidence the conjecture that the ether has been resuscitated.

4-7. Decaying-Exponential PWD Field

The chapter ends with a more detailed consideration of the electron's PWD field, assuming that it is a decaying exponential, as depicted in Fig. 4-8(a). The text would follow almost word-for-word the photon discussion of

Chap. 3 in connection with Fig. 3-9. The caption of Fig. 4-8 is sufficiently detailed to serve as the text with a minimum of further explanation.

The idea in Fig. 4-8 is that the PWD field has to be a good sine wave in order to get good destructive interference in the two-slit experiment.

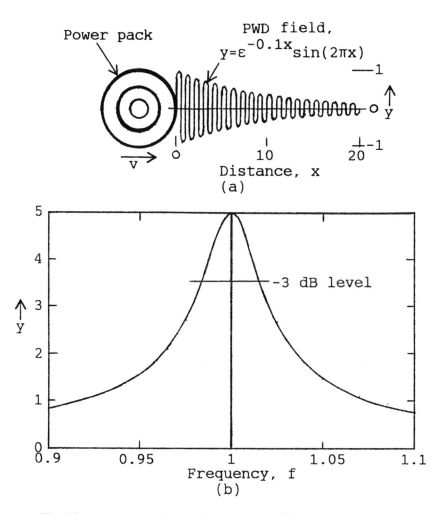

Fig. 4-8. A more detailed view of the electron's PWD field, assuming it is a decaying exponential. (a)Power pack and PWD field moving to the right with velocity v. The spatial frequency is 1 cycle/meter. (b)Spatial frequency spectrum of the PWD field, in cycles/meter. The Q is 31.

The spectrum of Fig. 4-8(a) is plotted in Fig. 4-8(b), with $f = \omega/2\pi$. This is a *spatial frequency* spectrum in cycles/meter rather than cycles/second.

All-important is the quality factor, or Q. The -3 dB level in Fig. 4-8(b) extends from $f = 0.9838$ to 1.0157, so $Q = 1/0.0319 = 31$; this is a reasonably high value.

Chapter 5

The Hydrogen Atom

5-1. Some Orbital Peculiarities

There are two ways in which the hydrogen atom strains quantum reality: First, the electron orbits are quantized, but it would be gratifying to be able to explain the forces that maintain stability as the electron completes a million cycles, say, in a particular orbit. Second, an electron moving in a wire, say, is accompanied by an electromagnetic field (EMF); but if it is in orbit around the hydrogen's proton nucleus, it does not form an EMF that radiates. Conjectural explanations for these two unusual characteristics are developed in the present chapter.

For elements in general, mathematical analysis and physical description become rapidly intractable as the atomic number increases. No attempt is therefore made to look beyond the hydrogen atom, but even here there are complications. Electron orbits are not circular for two reasons: the proton nucleus is not infinitely massive, so it executes a small orbit in conjunction with the electron's much larger orbit; and the electron orbit tends to be elliptical, filling all of local space with probabilities given by Schrodinger's quantum wavefunction. In what follows, the model of a hydrogen atom is simplified by assuming that the nucleus is an infinitely massive, stationary proton, and the electron orbits about this nucleus are circular.

5-2. Orbital Specifications

Compared to unrestricted planetary orbits, an unusual characteristic of the hydrogen atom is the fact that the electron's orbit is quantized; that is, the electron can only occupy certain restricted nominal values of orbital radius, which correspond to quantum numbers $n = 1, 2, 3, \ldots$. The smallest value, $n = 1$, is called the "ground state." Although quantized orbits are characteristic of all atoms in general, physicists long ago focused on hydrogen because it is a relatively simple example. Its orbital characteristics were explained by Niels Bohr in 1913. The reason for certain specific radii was largely solved by de Broglie, in 1924, with his hypothesis that a moving electron is accompanied by a particle-wave duality (PWD) field.

The experimental evidence is that the hydrogen electron's angular momentum is quantized. The angular momentum, $\mathcal{L}$, is the linear momentum, $m_0 v$, times radius, r, or

Angular momentum $(\mathcal{L})$ = mass $(m_0) \times$ velocity $(v) \times$ radius (r).

[Don't we have to use the relativistic mass, γm_0, in this equation? No, because it happens that the electron is not moving fast enough. According to Table 4-1, its velocity has to exceed 10^8 meters/second (or one-third the speed of light) before relativistic correction is warranted. This is all to the good—we have enough trouble without "relativistics" getting involved.] The specific quantization equation is

Angular momentum $(\mathcal{L})$ =

$$\frac{\text{quantum number } (n) \times \text{Planck's constant } (h)}{2\pi},$$

where Planck's constant $= 6.6261 \times 10^{-34}$ joule · second. Since n and 2π are dimensionless, the units of angular momentum are the same as those of Planck's constant, joule · second. For $n = 1$, $\mathcal{L} = h/(2\pi) = 1.055 \times 10^{-34}$ joule · second, and so forth. Numerical values of $\mathcal{L}$ versus n are given in the second column of Fig. 5-1.

The above equations are not complicated. But solve for the radius in these equations, and we get a mystery:

$$r = \frac{nh}{2\pi m_0 v}.$$

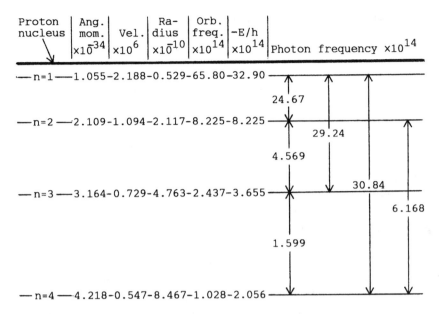

Fig. 5-1. Hydrogen electron quantum orbits represented by horizontal lines. The vertical spacing is proportional to the radius of each orbit. Units are meters, kilograms, seconds. Variations as a function of n are as follows: angular momentum $\propto n$; velocity $\propto 1/n$; radius $\propto n^2$; orbital frequency $\propto 1/n^3$; energy $\propto 1/n^2$. The difference between $-E/h$ levels determines the frequency of the photon that is involved in conserving energy balance.

Why should the orbital radius be restricted to these values of r? The solution to the mystery, it will turn out, is logical and simple.

The motion of the electron is governed by classical equations. The force of attraction between the electron and proton has to equal the centrifugal force. If we solve for the velocity, we get the values listed in the third column of Fig. 5-1. Notice that the velocity is inversely proportional to the quantum number. The highest velocity, with $n = 1$, is 2.188×10^6 meters/second; this is far below the 100×10^6 m/s at which, as noted above, relativistic effects should be taken into account.

If we solve for the orbital radius, we find that it is proportional to n^2. Figure 5-1 is drawn with the vertical scale proportional to the orbital radius. Since 10^{10} angstroms $= 1$ m, the values listed in the radius column give the radius directly in angstrom units. We see that the ground state radius, 0.529 Å, corresponds to a diameter of around 1 Å; this is, in fact, why angstrom units are convenient for atomic dimensions. (The diameter of a water molecule $\cong 3$ Å.)

Solving for the orbital frequency, we get

Orbital frequency (f_{orb}) =

$$\frac{\text{mass } (m_0) \times \text{velocity squared } (v^2)}{\text{quantum number } (n) \times \text{Planck's constant } (h)},$$

or

$$f_{orb} = \frac{m_0 v^2}{nh}.$$

The simplicity of this equation is important to an explanation for the quantum orbits. If we solve for numerical values, we find that f_{orb} is inversely proportional to n^3. Values for $n = 1$ to 4 are listed in Fig. 5-1. The $n = 1$ frequency, 65.8×10^{14} Hz, corresponds to an ultraviolet value. (f_{orb} is also given for $n = 1$ and 2 in connection with Fig. 2-1.)

It is convenient to include the electron's energy in Fig. 5-1. Energy is the ability to do work. Since energy has to be *supplied* to the electron to free it from the proton, by moving it towards $r = \infty$, the potential energy is negative. Added to the kinetic energy, we get for the *total* energy, simply,

$$E = \frac{m_0 v^2}{2}.$$

In Fig. 5-1, the energy column shows $-E/h$, or $-m_0 v^2/(2h)$. The advantage of this presentation is that the difference between any two quantum orbit E/h levels directly gives the frequency of the photon involved in conserving energy balance. The reason, of course, is that the frequency of a photon is given by E/h. For example, in going from $n = 2$ to $n = 1$ in Fig. 5-1, a photon of frequency $32.90 - 8.225 = 24.67$ ($\times 10^{14}$ Hz) is released, as is also shown in Fig. 2-1. If the electron is in the $n = 1$ orbit and it absorbs a photon whose frequency is 24.67×10^{14} Hz, it will jump (or spiral) to the $n = 2$ orbit, and so forth.

5-3. Stable Orbits Versus PWD Frequencies

Now we can consider a reasonable basis for the hydrogen electron orbits.

Recall the model of Fig. 4-5. My conjecture there is that the electron's PWD field consists of compression and expansion "winds" that are generated as the electron flies through the ether. The compressions and expansions do not convey any energy. Furthermore, in connection with the curved electron path of Fig. 4-6, it is conjectured that the ether contains streamlines that guide the electron. The lateral centripetal force that is required for a change in direction is supplied by the ether, but no exchange of energy is involved because there is no change in velocity. The streamline acts like a frictionless guide rail.

The PWD frequency of a moving electron is given in Chap. 4. For nonrelativistic velocity ($\gamma = 1$), we have

$$f_{PWD} = \frac{m_0 v^2}{h}.$$

Now compare this with the above equation for orbital frequency,

$$f_{orb} = \frac{m_0 v^2}{nh}.$$

We see that f_{PWD} is the nth harmonic of f_{orb}:

$$\text{At } n = 1, f_{PWD} = f_{orb};$$

$$\text{At } n = 2, f_{PWD} = 2f_{orb};$$

$$\text{At } n = 3, f_{PWD} = 3f_{orb},$$

and so forth. The above implies that the orbits are temporarily stable (typically for around 10^{-8} second) because of a simple resonance effect in which a standing wave, n cycles per orbit, confers stability. The ground state, $n = 1$, is of course most stable because f_{PWD} and f_{orb} are equal. Essentially, this is the model that de Broglie proposed.

What is a standing wave? Engineers are accustomed to working with electrical and mechanical standing waves. For example, in Fig. 3-2, close off the right end of the waveguide with a copper plate (a good short-circuit). When the wave traveling to the right strikes this end plate, it is reflected. We get a wave traveling to the left algebraically added to the wave traveling to the right. The result is the illusion of a "standing wave" because the "rms" (alternating current root-mean-square) voltage measured with a meter changes with distance, but not with time. It is zero at the short-circuit and at $\theta = 180°, 360°, \ldots$ to the left of the short-circuit, while the rms voltage is maximum at $\theta = 90°, 270°, \ldots$ to the left of the short-circuit.

Another way of looking at this is that, because of the short-circuit, the waveguide becomes a resonant chamber.

Is there an "everyday" example of a *mechanical* standing wave? The only one I can think of—an admittedly poor example because most people may not be aware of it—is the envelope of a vibrating violin string (or that of a similar instrument). One end, at the player's finger, is stationary. The other end, at the bridge, is also stationary. In between, the vibrating string's envelope forms the blurred half cycle of a sine wave. This is the standing wave, which does not change with time as long as the player holds the note constant.

Another way of looking at the hydrogen electron orbits is to compare wavelengths. The circumference of a hydrogen orbit is

$$\ell_{orb} = \frac{nh}{m_0 v},$$

while the wavelength of the PWD field is (from Chap. 4)

$$\lambda_{PWD} = \frac{h}{m_0 v}.$$

Therefore, as the electron flies along its orbit, it is responsible for a standing wave consisting of n cycles of the PWD field.

A standing wave would be formed by the electron traversing the same path over and over again, with only slight variations allowed from one orbit to the next. (For $n = 1$ the path could be an ellipse, and so forth.) Three possibilities are illustrated, in Fig. 5-2, for the $n = 4$ orbit:

In (a), the PWD field is a transverse vibration, in a radial direction. The electron swings away from, and towards, the nucleus four times per orbit.

In (b), the PWD field is again a transverse vibration, but the electron swings occur at right angles to the orbital plane. (A side view is depicted in which the posterior locus overlaps the anterior locus, except for a reversal in direction.)

In (c), the PWD field is longitudinal, with compressions and expansions similar to those of a sound wave. The thick and thin orbital regions symbolize the fact that the electron speeds up and slows down four times per orbit.

Which of the orbital representations is most reasonable? Mode (a) is reasonable because it leads naturally to an orbital change when the electron spirals from the $n = 4$ to $n = 3$ (or any other) orbit. Mode (b) is possible because there is a restoring force if the electron veers away from the orbital plane. The longitudinal mode of (c) requires a perfectly elastic ether to speed up and slow down the electron as it flies around an approximately circular orbit.

The integer relation between orbital and PWD field frequencies is further illustrated in Fig. 5-3. It is easiest to represent longitudinal vibrations, in which the electrons speed up and slow down n times per orbit, via the thick and thin orbital regions of mode (c) of Fig. 5-2, but the intention is that these lines should also represent modes (a) or (b).

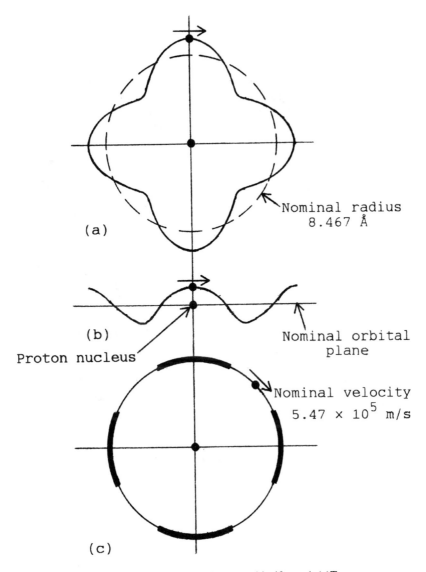

(a)

Nominal radius
8.467 Å

(b)

Proton nucleus

Nominal orbital
plane

Nominal velocity
5.47×10^5 m/s

(c)

Fig. 5-2.   Three possible hydrogen electron orbits if $n = 4$: (a)Transverse radial. The electron swings away from, and towards, the nucleus n times per orbit. (b)Transverse transradial. The electron swings occur at right angles to the orbital plane. (c)Longitudinal. The thick and thin orbital regions symbolize the fact that the electron speeds up and slows down n times per orbit.

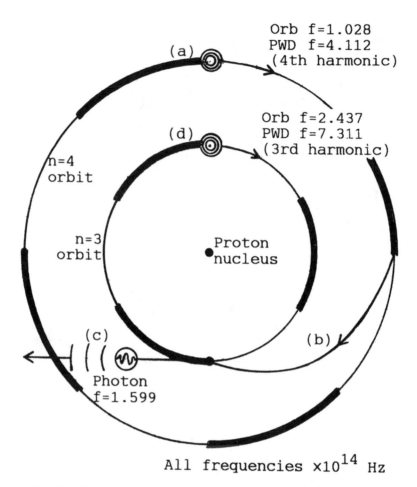

Orb f=1.028
PWD f=4.112
(4th harmonic)

(a)

Orb f=2.437
PWD f=7.311
(3rd harmonic)

(d)

n=4
orbit

n=3
orbit

Proton
nucleus

(c)

Photon
f=1.599

(b)

All frequencies $\times 10^{14}$ Hz

Fig. 5-3.   Four frames, (a) to (d), of scenario in which a hydrogen electron
descends from $n = 4$ to $n = 3$ orbit. It is easiest to draw longitudinal vibrations, in which the electron speeds up and slows down
n times per orbit, via the thick and thin orbital lines of mode (c) of
Fig. 5-2, but the intention is that these lines should also represent
modes (a) or (b). (a)Electron is temporarily locked into the $n = 4$
orbit because of four cycles of a standing wave, since $f_{PWD} = 4f_{orb}$.
(b)Electron falls out of the $n = 4$ orbit, and gradually spirals in towards the nucleus. (c)To conserve energy balance, a photon of frequency 1.599×10^{14} Hz is launched. (d)The electron temporarily
locks into the $n = 3$ orbit because of three cycles of a standing
wave, since $f_{PWD} = 3f_{orb}$.

In Fig. 5-3(a), we have the hydrogen electron in the $n = 4$ orbit, with $f_{orb} = 1.028$ and $f_{PWD} = 4f_{orb} = 4.112$ (all frequencies have to be multiplied by 10^{14} Hz). The electron's PWD field is (nominally) a compression wind in the ether, traveling at the velocity of the electron, of course (values are given in the third column of Fig. 5-1). The photon's wave-particle duality (WPD) field is (nominally) a compression shock wave in the ether, symbolized by a few arcs preceding the photon, the entire assembly traveling at the speed of light.

In Fig. 5-3, (a) to (d) are meant to illustrate four different frames of a typical scenario. After 10^6 orbits in (a), (plenty of time for the electron to visit all regions of Schrodinger's probability space), the electron falls out of the $n = 4$ orbit. The usual quantum description is that it "jumps," say, to the $n = 3$ orbit. Since my conjecture is that there is nothing exotic about the hydrogen electron orbits—they are simply examples of ordinary resonance effects supported by standing waves—the electron locus in (b) is depicted as a gradual spiral.

According to Fig. 5-1, in descending from $n = 4$ to $n = 3$, the electron's velocity increases from 0.547 to 0.729 ($\times 10^6$ meters/second) and the orbital radius decreases from 8.467 to 4.763 angstroms. To conserve energy balance, the electron launches a photon, (c), whose frequency is 1.599 ($\times 10^{14}$ Hz). Finally, (d), the electron temporarily locks into the $n = 3$ orbit, with $f_{orb} = 2.437$ and $f_{PWD} = 3f_{orb} = 7.311$ ($\times 10^{14}$ Hz).

To summarize: Some kind of mysterious "substance"—the ether—behaves somewhat like a jelly. Each hydrogen atom electron orbit is characterized by n standing waves carved out of the jelly; that is, each cycle follows the same path over and over again except for small, gradual changes. When the path strays too far from a stable locus, the jelly gives way, allowing the electron to spiral to a lower value of n (and the excess energy is released in the form of a photon). When $n = 1$, the single standing wave is maintained indefinitely.

5-4. Synchrotron Radiation

Since a moving electron is an electric current, it is accompanied by a magnetic field. A simple illustration of how an electron in the circular orbit inside a coil, say, generates an alternating magnetic field, is given in Fig. 5-4. [Because of an optical illusion, the orbits of (a), (b), and (c) appear not to be lined up vertically; actually, (b) and (c) are side views of (a).] In view (b), the electron is coming out of the page, and the associated magnetic field lines are clockwise as shown. At an external point P, in particular, the lines are moving downward. View (c) is a "photograph" taken 180°

later; the electron is going into the page. Now the magnetic field lines are counterclockwise. At point P, the lines are moving upward.

There is thus an alternating field generated by the electron. Notice that the magnetic field *inside* the circular path is unidirectional, with lines always moving upward.

Electrons can be used to generate a dc field, which is also a form of energy, but much more significant from this point of view is the fact that the hydrogen electron's field is alternating. In accordance with Maxwell's equations, a changing magnetic field generates a changing electric field that generates a changing magnetic field etc. In short, we end up with an electromagnetic field (EMF). The mystery is that a captured electron—an electron that is in orbit around a proton nucleus—does not form an EMF; it rotates in silence!

Yet the same electron, moving around a manmade circular path, *does* generate an EMF, as expected. In fact, the EMF radiation, known as synchrotron radiation, has important applications for research in physics, chemistry, biology, and medicine. This is because it can create high-energy beams ranging from infrared to X-ray frequencies. To generate the radiation, high-density electron beams, almost at the speed of light, in accelerator storage rings, are made to execute circular paths under the influence of powerful bending magnets.

The important point is that the EMF energy radiated away has to come from the electron's kinetic energy. In a synchrotron, the energy is resupplied by acceleration devices. In a hydrogen atom, the electron does not radiate; if it did, it would gradually slow down and fall into the positive nucleus.

Figure 5-3 can be used to illuminate the synchrotron radiation mystery of the hydrogen electron. In Fig. 5-3, do the following thought experiment: Remove the proton nucleus and replace it with a magnetic field that is at right angles to, and into, the page. If the field is strong enough, it can maintain the electron's circular orbit unchanged. The difference is that, with a proton nucleus, the electron does not display synchrotron radiation; with a magnetic field replacement, it does. Synchrotron radiation occurs when an electron is forced into a partially circular orbit (by a bending magnet or any other means).

It is interesting to calculate the magnetic field that is needed for the above "thought experiment." The required centripetal force is given by

Force $(F) =$

$$\frac{\text{electrostatic constant } (k) \times \text{electron charge squared } (e^2)}{\text{radius squared } (r^2)}.$$

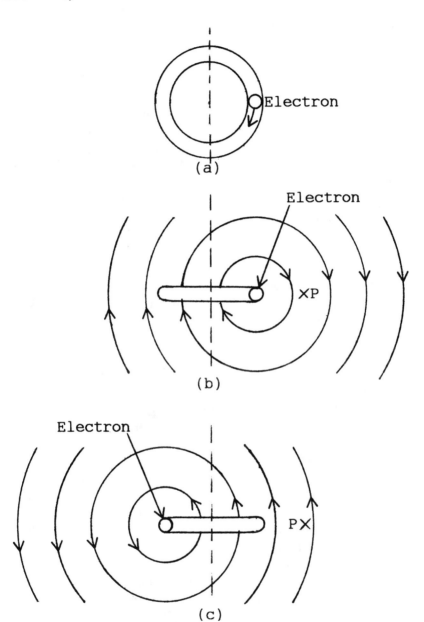

Fig. 5-4. The magnetic field associated with an electron that is in a circular orbit: (a)The electron moving clockwise. (b)Side view of (a). The electron is coming out of the page, and magnetic field lines are clockwise. (c)Side view of (a), but 180° later. Now the electron is going into the page, and magnetic field lines are counterclockwise. At point P, the field has reversed.

The force acting on a charge (in this case e) that is moving in a magnetic field is

Force (F) = flux density (B) × electron charge (e) × velocity (v),

where B is the *magnetic* flux density. For the ground state, $n = 1$, the calculations reveal that the flux density needed to maintain an electron in an $n = 1$ orbit is 235,100 teslas (T). This is a completely unrealistic, unobtainable value. A normal, strong magnetic flux density is around 2 T (but 60-T pulsed fields have been reported). Because the required density varies as $1/n^3$, we have to go to $n = 50$ to get a reasonable value, $B = 1.88$ T.

If anything, the huge B values indicate that the hydrogen electron should be an excellent synchrotron radiator. Something radically changes when an electron is captured by a proton to form a hydrogen atom.

My conjecture is this: The ether surrounding a proton nucleus contains spherical stream lines. When the proton captures an electron, the latter, and the compression wind it creates, fly through the ether along one of the streamlines. If the electron happens to be in the $n = 4$ orbit, the velocity is (see Fig. 5-1) 0.547×10^6 meters/second; if the electron is in the $n = 1$ orbit, its velocity is 2.188×10^6 m/s, and so forth. But—and this is the heart of the matter—the stream line acts like the above-mentioned frictionless guide rail. The electron slides along the "frictionless guide rail" without attenuation. (This is admittedly far-fetched, but it is well to remember the unbelievable characteristics also displayed in superconductivity and superfluidity).

Why does this suppress synchrotron radiation? In the above "thought experiment," the magnetic field of the electron interacts with the 235,100 T external field; this slows the electron, and its lost kinetic energy is converted into synchrotron radiation. But if an electron is in one of the stable orbits surrounding a proton, its magnetic field does not have to interact with another field. The electron is stably held in its nominally circular path by the "ethereal" streamlines. The electron maintains its circular orbit not by a pull from the proton nucleus, but by a lateral centripetal push exerted by those "frictionless guide rails." *From the electron's point of view,* it is not accelerating, so its orbit can be represented by a straight-line trajectory, as in Fig. 5-1.

A second equally far-fetched explanation is that the space surrounding the hydrogen's nucleus is "uncurved." We are somewhat familiar with the curvature of cosmological space involving massive stars and black holes. This second conjecture is that an observer traveling with a hydrogen electron would see a straight-line trajectory rather than a circular orbit.

We have come to think of the curvature of space as an exotic effect based on Albert Einstein's theory of relativity; a rare phenomenon that can ordinarily be ignored, yielding a small curvature that can only be measured with highly sophisticated equipment. The conjecture here is that, on the contrary, the curvature of space is at the heart of every proton. Far from being a rare phenomenon, we are, literally, constructed out of curved space!

The curvature of space is a central theme in Section 8-8 of Chapter 8.

The "straight-line" trajectory of Fig. 5-1 gives us another way of looking at the Pauli exclusion principle [Wolfgang Pauli (1900–1958)]. According to this, more than one electron may not simultaneously occupy the same quantum state. Extending Fig. 5-1, the helium atom would appear to be two-dimensional, with an electron locus above, as well as below, the central nucleus line. Atoms between lithium (3 electrons) and neon (10 electrons) can be represented by the end view of Fig. 5-5, in which a central nucleus is surrounded by eight 45° sectors, each of which can hold an electron in the $n = 2$

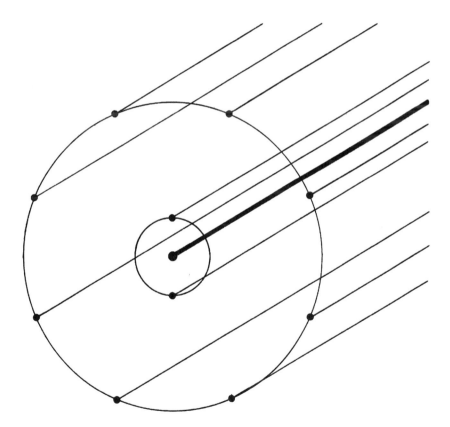

Fig. 5-5.   Straight-line trajectory representation of the neon atom. It has two electrons in the $n = 1$ level, and eight electrons in the $n = 2$ level.

level (since the two 180° sectors of the $n = 1$ level are full). Pauli's principle excludes more than eight 45° sectors for the $n = 2$ level, and so forth.

To summarize: (a) Because of the lateral centripetal support provided by a putative ethereal jelly, or (b) because the space surrounding the nucleus is "uncurved," the electron behaves as if it is traveling in a straight line. In the absence of radial acceleration, it no longer generates EMF synchrotron radiation.

It seems to me that these conjectures are not more bizarre than the many-parallel-universes proposal of Hugh Everett III (1957) (and recently revived by D. Deutsch, 1997).

Chapter 6

Bell's Theorem

6-1. Twin-State Photon Generator

In certain experiments involving pairs of photons, to be described below, it appears as if an action visited upon one of the photons is instantaneously felt by the other photon, even if it is relatively far away. John S. Bell pointed out that the correlation between the two photons exceeded the expectation allowed by a local (speed of light) phenomenon [J. S. Bell, 1964, 1987]. Bell's theorem states that certain experimental results *must* be non-local; i.e., they display superluminal (faster-than-light) behavior. In this chapter, two of the representative experiments are considered.

But superluminal transmission of information is strictly forbidden in electromagnetic field theory, as well as by common sense. According to Bell, if the experimenter imparts a change to photon C, it can almost instantaneously cause a corresponding change to photon D, millions of meters away. It appears as if an explanation requires conjectures that bypass quantum mechanics.

The first experiment is based on the block diagram of Fig. 6-1. Here the central block is a twin-state photon generator. There are several ways to generate a *single pair* of photons: For many elements, if the atoms are placed into an excited state, their outer electrons emit a pair of photons when they return to their ground state (in contrast with the hydrogen atom of Fig. 2-1, where the single electron can only launch a single photon).

Favorite sources are mercury excited by an electron beam and calcium excited by a laser beam. The two emitted photons have different frequencies: For the calcium cascade, we have $f = 5.438 \times 10^{14}$ Hz (yellow-green) and 7.092×10^{14} Hz (indigo-violet). The different colors are of little consequence. The important aspect of twin-state emission is that both photons have the same polarization angle, ϕ, as indicated in Fig. 6-1. (Actually, because the net angular momentum of the photon pair must be zero, the photons are emitted with opposite angular momentums, but this translates into the same value of ϕ insofar as the experiment is concerned.)

The actual polarization angle *varies randomly* from $-90°$ to $+90°$, but left and right photons have the *same* ϕ.

Eventually, after traveling a relatively large distance, the photons enter calcite filters A and B. The distance is "relatively large" in the sense that the time taken for a signal to travel between A and B is appreciable, even at the speed of light. For example, a distance of 3 meters requires 10 nanoseconds, but this time is appreciable, and it can be measured easily with a sophisticated electronic clock.

6-2. Calcite Filters

Shine a small-diameter ray of visible light onto the surface of a slab of glass. Let the angle between the ray and normal (perpendicular line) to the surface be θ_1. Going from air into glass, the speed of light is reduced; this causes the ray to bend so that, in the glass, θ_2 is less than θ_1. (The ray bends towards the normal.) The action is described by Snell's law:

$$\frac{\text{sine of } \theta_1}{\text{sine of } \theta_2} = \frac{\text{velocity in medium 1}}{\text{velocity in medium 2}}.$$

If medium 1 is air (or a vacuum), the velocity in medium 1 is $c \cong 3 \times 10^8$ m/s, and the velocity ratio is called the index of refraction. The index is always greater than 1.

If, instead of glass, we use an anisotropic, birefringent material, such as calcite (calcium carbonate), something unusual occurs. As "birefringent" implies, the calcite has *two* indices of refraction. In general, two rays, corresponding to two different values of θ_2, form at the interface between say, air and calcite.

There is more to it than this, however. It turns out that, if the polarization of one of the internal rays is horizontal, say, then the polarization

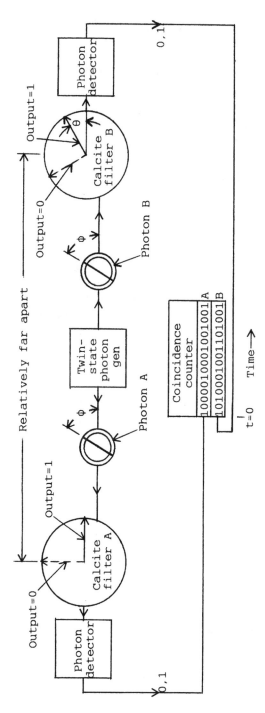

Fig. 6-1. Experiment from which it is concluded that photons A and B somehow communicate with each other superluminally. The photons are simultaneously emitted by the twin-state photon generator; although their polarization angle ϕ is a random variable, ϕ is the same for both photons. The calcite filter angles are set to $\theta_A = 0$ on the left and, manually, to $\theta_B = \theta$ on the right. Depending on ϕ versus θ_A or θ_B, respectively, each photon exits the filter either along the 1 or 0 output paths. A coincidence counter keeps track of simultaneous matches between A and B outputs.

of the second ray is vertical. The polarization angle between the two rays always has a difference of 90°.

Recall that a ray of light is an electromagnetic field (EMF), with $\underline{E}$ and $\underline{H}$ lines perpendicular to each other and to the direction of propagation, as illustrated in Fig. 3-2. The polarization angle is determined, by definition, by the direction of the $\underline{E}$ lines. Therefore, shine a small-diameter ray (it need not be visible light) onto the surface of a slab of calcite. Let the angle between the ray and normal to the surface be θ_1. Inside the calcite, two rays form. We can orient the slab so that θ_{2H} is a horizontally polarized component, while θ_{2V} is a vertically polarized component.

The applied (incident) ray, in general, splits into two vector components, inside the calcite, to form θ_{2H} and θ_{2V} rays. If the applied ray is horizontally polarized, all of it will (ideally) form the θ_{2H} ray, leaving nothing for the θ_{2V} ray, and so forth.

Next, we carry on in the tradition set forth in Chap. 3: We block the light source so effectively that only one isolated photon at a time gets through. Since the photon is the irreducible constituent of an EMF, it cannot split into two vector components. How does the photon avoid a split personality? It will probably follow the path that is *closest* to its angle of polarization.

To illustrate with numerical values, using standard four-quadrant angle orientation: Let the polarization of the input photon be ϕ, where ϕ lies between $-90°$ and $+90°$. (Angles outside of this range can always be extended into the range. For example, 120° is the same as $-60°$; $-135°$ is the same as $+45°$, and so forth.) Then some simple sketches will show that

If ϕ lies between $-45°$ and $+45°$, the internal ray follows the θ_{2H} path;

If ϕ lies between $+45°$and $+90°$, the internal ray follows the θ_{2V} path;

If ϕ lies between $-90°$ and $-45°$, the internal ray follows the θ_{2V} path.

In Fig. 6-1, to avoid confusion regarding H and V rays when they are not actually horizontal and vertical, the H and V subscripts are abandoned. Instead, one internal ray is shown as a solid line and its output is labeled "1"; the other is a dashed line and its output is labeled "0." The solid-line direction for calcite filter A is along the x axis ($\theta_A = 0$), but B's direction is a manually adjustable angle, θ_B. Therefore, in what follows, the calcite *difference* angle, $\theta = \theta_B - \theta_A$, is equal to θ_B.

The manually-adjustable θ can range from 0° to 90°, while the incoming polarization angle, ϕ, can range from $-90°$ to $+90°$, as noted previously. The path that the internal ray follows (1 or 0) depends upon the difference, $\phi - \theta$. This can range from

$$\phi = -90°, \theta = 90°, \text{ so that } \phi - \theta = -180°$$

to

$$\phi = +90°, \theta = 0°, \text{ so that } \phi - \theta = 90°.$$

This can become very confusing because of the mixture of positive and negative values, but it turns out that the *magnitude* of $\phi - \theta$, or $|\phi - \theta|$, is the important variable because the internal ray "will probably follow the path that is *closest* to its angle of polarization." Here is the revised set of rules (notice the absence of negative values), given by $|\phi - \theta|$:

If $|\phi - \theta|$ lies between $0°$ and $45°$, the internal ray follows the 1 path;

If $|\phi - \theta|$ lies between $45°$ and $135°$, the internal ray follows the 0 path;

If $|\phi - \theta|$ lies between $135°$ and $180°$, the internal ray follows the 1 path.

(The cases $|\phi - \theta|$ *exactly* $= 45°$ or $135°$ are statistically insignificant.) In Fig. 6-1, $\phi = 60°$ and $\theta_A = 0°$, so $|\phi - \theta| = 60°$ and filter A's output is 0. For filter B, $\phi = 60°$ and $\theta_B = \theta = 30°$, so $|\phi - \theta| = 30°$ and filter B's output is 1.

In Table 6-1, ϕ goes from $-82.5°, -67.5°, \ldots, +82.5°$ as θ goes from $0°, 15°, \ldots, 90°$. The only way for you to get unconfused is to check some of my answers (which are, of course, never wrong). The table gives the outputs (0 or 1) of calcite filters A and B, and also a matching value, $M = 1$, if the filter outputs are the same.

The reason for this procedure is that the photons appear at random time intervals, and with random values of polarization ϕ (unlike the orderly entries of Table 6-1). The easiest way to handle the random stream of data is to use the coincidence counter of Fig. 6-1. The counter gives the number of matches M $(0,0 + 1,1)$ and also the number of mismatches $(0,1 + 1,0)$.

A final note concerning the equipment: The calcite filter's output is useless unless it can be converted into an electrical signal. Accordingly, each filter feeds a detector in the form of a photomultiplier. The latter is sensitive enough to respond to a reasonable fraction of entering photons. In practice, one must use two photomultipliers, one for the 1 output and the other for the 0 output. To simplify the diagram, however, a single "photon detector" block is shown; it merely converts the filter's 0s and 1s into electrical 0s and 1s.

Table 6-1. Expected coincidence counter matches in Fig. 6-1 as the photons' polarization angle, ϕ, takes on values of $-82.5°$, $-67.5°$, ..., $+82.5°$ while the calcite filter difference angle is set for $0°$, $15°$, ..., $90°$. The A columns represent the output of the A filter, which remains the same for the entire table because it is not rotated. The B column, however, rotates down one row distance, $\phi = 15°$, as we move to the right one θ column distance, $\theta = 15°$. The M columns list the number of matches.

Filter difference angle, θ

Photon polarization angle ϕ	$0°$			$15°$			$30°$			$45°$			$60°$			$75°$			$90°$		
	A	B	M	A	B	M	A	B	M	A	B	M	A	B	M	A	B	M	A	B	M
$-82.5°$	0	0	1	0	0	1	0	0	1	0	0	1	0	1		0	1		0	1	
$-67.5°$	0	0	1	0	0	1	0	0	1	0	0	1	0	0	1	0	1		0	1	
$-52.5°$	0	0	1	0	0	1	0	0	1	0	0	1	0	0	1	0	0	1	0	1	
$-37.5°$	1	1	1	1	0		1	0		1	0		1	0		1	0		1	0	
$-22.5°$	1	1	1	1	1	1	1	0		1	0		1	0		1	0		1	0	
$-7.5°$	1	1	1	1	1	1	1	1	1	1	0		1	0		1	0		1	0	
$7.5°$	1	1	1	1	1	1	1	1	1	1	1	1	1	0		1	0		1	0	
$22.5°$	1	1	1	1	1	1	1	1	1	1	1	1	1	1	1	1	0		1	0	
$37.5°$	1	1	1	1	1	1	1	1	1	1	1	1	1	1	1	1	1	1	1	0	
$52.5°$	0	0	1	0	1		0	1		0	1		0	1		0	1		0	1	
$67.5°$	0	0	1	0	0	1	0	1		0	1		0	1		0	1		0	1	
$82.5°$	0	0	1	0	0	1	0	0	1	0	1		0	1		0	1		0	1	
M totals			12			10			8			6			4			2			0

6-3. Experiment Using Calcite Filters

Now consider the gathering of typical experimental data [J. F. Clauser and A. Shimony, 1978; A. Aspect et al., 1982]. In the following numerical example,

$$\theta_B \text{ is set to } 30°:$$

Starting at $t = 0$, because ϕ randomly varies between $-90°$ and $+90°$, we get a string of 0s and 1s. In Fig. 6-1, the A output is 1 0 0 . . . 0 0 1. With $\theta = 30°$, the B output is 1 0 1 . . . 0 0 1. Out of the string of 16 binary digits, the coincidence counter shows that M (the number of matches) is 12, corresponding to $M = 75\%$.

What do we expect? Since ϕ is a random variable between $-90°$ and $+90°$, we can take representative samples 15° apart, say, such as at $-82.5°$, $-67.5°$, . . . , $+82.5°$, as depicted in the rows of Table 6-1. The columns represent calcite filter difference angle $\theta = 0°$, 15°, . . . , 90°. The A columns represent the output of the A filter, which remains the same for the entire table because it is not rotated. The B column, however, rotates down one row distance, $\phi = 15°$, as we move to the right one column distance, $\theta = 15°$. The M totals appear to follow a linear decrease: 12, 10, 8, . . . 2, 0, as θ linearly increases.

The following illustrate some of the Table 6-1 entries in the

$$\theta = 75° \text{ column:}$$

$\phi = -82.5°, \theta_A = 0°,$ $|\phi - \theta| = $ 82.5°, A output $= 0$;
$\phi = -82.5°, \theta_B = \theta = 75°,$ $|\phi - \theta| = $ 157.5°, B output $= 1$ ($M = 0$)

$\phi = -22.5°, \theta_A = 0°,$ $|\phi - \theta| = $ 22.5°, A output $= 1$;
$\phi = -22.5°, \theta_B = \theta = 75°,$ $|\phi - \theta| = $ 97.5°, B output $= 0$ ($M = 0$)

$\phi = 52.5°, \theta_A = 0°,$ $|\phi - \theta| = $ 52.5°, A output $= 0$;
$\phi = 52.5°, \theta_B = \theta = 75°,$ $|\phi - \theta| = $ 22.5°, B output $= 1$ ($M = 0$)

The straight-line plot of M_{total} as a function of θ is shown as the "expected" curve in Fig. 6-2(a). The "measured" curve is also shown; it is given by $M_{total} = 12\cos^2\theta$. Quantum theory, as usual, agrees with the experimental observations by predicting a variation that also has a $\cos^2\theta$ shape.

Bell's assertion that superluminal effects are occurring is based on the curves of Fig. 6-2(a). At $\theta = 15°$, for example, we expect a coincidence probability of $M = 10/12 = 83\%$; instead, we measure a probability of

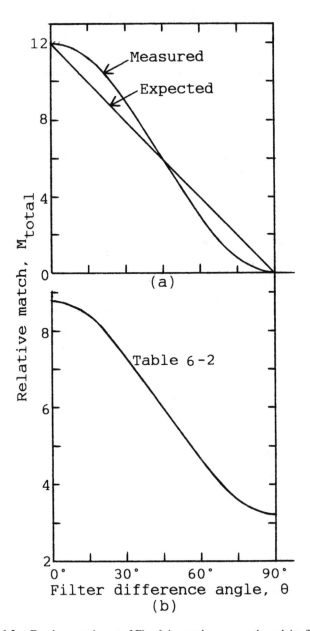

Fig. 6-2. For the experiment of Fig. 6-1, matches versus the calcite filters' difference angle, θ: (a)Expected matches as given by Table 6-1, and the values actually measured. The latter is a plot of $12\cos^2\theta$. (b)Expected matches as given by Table 6-2.

$M = 11.2/12 = 93\%$. At $\theta = 30°$, we expect $M = 8/12 = 67\%$; instead, we measure $M = 9/12 = 75\%$; and so forth. Since the calcite filter outputs have a much higher coincidence than expected, even though they are physically very far apart, there must be, *somehow,* instantaneous communication between the calcite filters (so the argument goes). My argument, however, is that this nonsensical conclusion only *proves* that there is something wrong with Table 6-1.

Among people who pay attention to such matters, the discrepancy between measured and expected curves of Fig. 6-2 has become a traumatic experience. Visualize the following scenario: The calcite filters in Fig. 6-1 are 10^6 meters apart. The experimenter, Z, rotates calcite filter B to the $\theta = 0$ position. The coincidence counter reads "$M = 100\%$." So far so good. Then Z rotates filter B to the $\theta = 15°$ position. Z expects "$M = 83\%$"; instead, Z gets "$M = 93\%$." Z checks everything carefully, but there are no errors. The conclusion is inescapable that, at the $15°$ setting, the A and B photons are connected to each other through a medium that is 10^6 meters long. Superluminal effects!

Since photons are minuscule, the connection between A and B must be some sort of "string" or "cable." To avoid offending the cosmological "string theory" people, I will call the inter-photon connection a "cable." This may offend electrical engineers, but they will not take the cable proposal too seriously, and will rapidly "hang up" on it.

The photons somehow communicate with each other superluminally through the cable. When photon A exits calcite filter A along the "output 1" path, it *instantaneously* tells this to photon B; the latter, if it was headed for the "output 0" path of filter B, *instantaneously* "changes its mind," and exits along the "output 1" path. Similarly, when photon A exits filter A along the "output 0" path, it instructs photon B, if it was headed for the "output 1" path, to instantaneously change its mind and exit along the "output 0" path of filter B.

Well, almost. Let us not be unrealistic by expecting perfect agreement between photons A and B. If the discrepancy between their calcite positions is too large, one may exit through "output 1" while the other ends up going through "output 0." However, 93% of the time, when $\theta = 15°$, their calcite exits are in agreement.

What is the reaction of physicists to the news that photons A and B can instantaneously control each other's movements over vast distances? Three representative quotations are given in Chap. 1; the reader should draw his or her own conclusions.

Bell's theorem unleashed a tremendous amount of work—theoretical, experimental, and what one may call philosophical. Experimentally, the discrepancy between measured and expected curves of Fig. 6-2 has been verified beyond doubt. In the next section, however, I present two different conjectures for explaining how $M = 93\%$, at $\theta = 15°$, without resorting to superluminal message velocities along semi-infinitely-long cables (and without resorting to extrasensory perception, ectoplasm, and so forth).

6-4. Two Conjectures That Can Explain the Discrepancy

The difficulty with Table 6-1 is that its entries demonstrate "all-or-nothing" behavior. Suppose that the experiment is conducted, with $\theta_A = \theta_B = 0°$, until 1000 photon pairs are generated in the twin-state block of Fig. 6-1. The polarization ϕ of 500 pairs will fall between $-45°$ and $+45°$, and Table 6-1 would have us believe that *each* of them yields $A = B = 1$, $M = 1$; for the other 500 pairs, the polarization magnitude is greater than $45°$, so *each* of them yields $A = B = 0$, and again $M = 1$.

On the other hand, consider the rough treatment that an *individual photon* suffers as it travels through a calcite filter: Its $\underline{E}$ (and $\underline{H}$) lines are rotated, *by as much as 45°*, until the polarization of the internal ray agrees with that of the filter. What I am leading up to, in other words, is that the filter is somewhat imperfect, and the polarization angle of a photon is not a sacred, inviolate constant. It is a trivial matter, in waveguide structures, to change the polarization angle by as much as we please: Simply take a long section of the waveguide of Fig. 3-2, and *gradually* twist it so that the rotation, per cycle of EMF, is reasonably small. It is quite common, in waveguide assemblies, for one reason or another, to require a polarization angle rotation of 90°.

(a) The "Fig. 6-3(b)" conjecture: My first conjecture is that, because of the "rough treatment," the photon's polarization angle is subject to small perturbations ($\pm 7.5°$ out of 180°, or $\pm 4.2\%$, is used as an example below). Recall the models of Figs. 3-6 and 3-7: A photon is preceded by a (nominal) compression shock wave as it plows through the ether at the speed of light, and the ether contains streamlines that can guide the photon, depending on slit openings and interference effects. The conjecture is that, in addition to lateral push in an interference apparatus, the ethereal

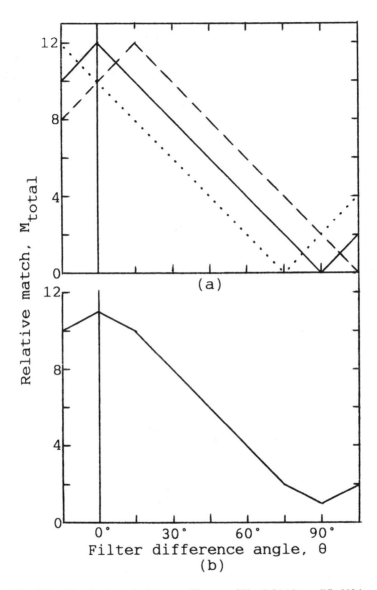

Fig. 6-3. Showing how the "expected" curve of Fig. 6-2(a) is modified if the
ϕ polarization angles of photons A and B randomly shift by $\pm7.5°$
before they leave their calcite filters. (a)The shifts are equivalent
to moving the curve 15° to the right (- - - -), or 15° to the left
($\cdots$), or leaving it alone (——). (b)The result if the ordinate
values of (a) are added in accordance with Eq. (6-1).

streamlines can *slightly* rotate the photon's plane of polarization. In Fig. 6-1, this can even happen in a short flight on the way to the calcite filter, and/or it can occur inside the filter. (The latter possibility seems more reasonable to me.) Whether, and by how much, ϕ is rotated depends on the statistically random but predetermined history of the photon. (Remember, also, that the twin-state photons have appreciably different frequencies and energies.)

In Fig. 6-1, let us suppose that ϕ_A and ϕ_B can each change by, say, 7.5°. What does this do to the "expected" curve of Fig. 6-2(a)? To investigate this in a way that is tractable, suppose that ϕ_A and ϕ_B each randomly and *independently* switch ±7.5° with respect to their nominal angle. The probability is ¼, then, that each of the following four combinations will occur:

$$\phi_A + 7.5°, \phi_B + 7.5°, \phi \text{ difference} = 0;$$

$$\phi_A + 7.5°, \phi_B - 7.5°, \phi \text{ difference} = 15°;$$

$$\phi_A - 7.5°, \phi_B + 7.5°, \phi \text{ difference} = -15°;$$

$$\phi_A - 7.5°, \phi_B - 7.5°, \phi \text{ difference} = 0.$$

This is equivalent to switching the calcite filter difference angle, θ, as follows:

25% of the time, add 15° to θ;

25% of the time, subtract 15° from θ;   (6-1)

50% of the time, no change in θ.

On Fig. 6-2(a), the above is equivalent to moving the curve to the right by 15° [curve is represented by a dashed line in Fig. 6-3(a)]; to the left by 15° [curve is represented by a dotted line in Fig. 6-3(a)]; and leaving it alone [curve is represented by a solid line in Fig. 6-3(a)]. When we add the M values in accordance with the above Eq. (6-1), we get the piecewise-linear curve of Fig. 6-3(b).

The curve of Fig. 6-3(b) is reasonably similar, in *shape*, to the $\cos^2\theta$ "measured" curve of Fig. 6-2(a). The main point of the above exercise is to show that small (±7.5°) random shifts in the polarization angle, if they occur before the twin photons reach their detectors, can approximate the $\cos^2\theta$ function. The experimenter has no way of knowing that the polarization angle of photon A disagrees with that of photon B. This leads to the false and impossible conclusion that the twin photons are instantaneously communicating with each other so as to obtain greater than expected correlation, or probability of matches, when $|\theta| < 45°$.

In a previous version of this chapter that was submitted for publication, a reviewer commented that the author introduces a conjecture that,

> the author thinks, will solve the problem: small random perturbations of the polarization of the photons. The difficulty with this idea—which is of course very natural and can take all kinds of forms (random fluctuation of the index of refraction, an ether as here, random fluctuations of some parameters in the detectors, etc.)—is that it does not solve any difficulty. The reason is that such fluctuations can easily be included in the proof of the Bell theorem. In other words, if these fluctuations exist and modify the observed correlations, they will not allow one to escape the limitations imposed by the Bell theorem—except of course if they have a nonlocal character, but then one does not gain anything by invoking them.

It seems to me that the inclusion of fluctuations, in a proof of Bell's theorem, is unproven conjecture. The notion that one photon can instantaneously influence another is, to repeat, nonsense. Instead of thinking that this is "somehow" possible, we should seek to escape the trap set by Bell's theorem.

(b) The "Fig. 6-2(b)" conjecture: Let us assume that a more probabilistic polarization perspective is reasonable, so that the polarization angle of a photon can change within limits determined by some kind of probability density curve, such as Gaussian or linear [L. Mandel, 1983]. A linear curve is illustrated by the schedule of Table 6-2, where it is assumed that the A column probabilities are, reading downwards, 0, 0.2, 0.4, $\ldots$, 1, $\ldots$. This also determines the B column probabilities. (There is no experimental basis for these values. They are only meant to depict one reasonable possibility.)

$$With \ \theta_A = \theta_B = 0°:$$

If photon pair polarization ϕ is approximately $\pm 7.5°$, the photons will follow, as before, paths $A = B = 1$, $M = 1$. But if the polarization ϕ is approximately $\pm 22.5°$, the Table 6-2 entries show that only 80% will follow path $A = 1$; the remaining 20% follow path $A = 0$. The values in the A and B columns of Table 6-2 now stand for

$$A = \text{probability that photon will follow path 1 of filter } A,$$
$$1 - A = \text{probability that photon will follow path 0 of filter } A,$$
$$B = \text{probability that photon will follow path 1 of filter } B,$$
$$1 - B = \text{probability that photon will follow path 0 of filter } B.$$

Table 6-2. The same as Table 6-1 except that the column A and B entries now represent the *probability* that the photon will exit in the calcite's 1 direction. The M columns list the joint probability of a match assuming that the exact choice of each photon is independent of that of its twin.

Photon polariz. angle, ϕ	Filter difference angle, θ											
	0°			15°			30°			45°		
	A	B	M	A	B	M	A	B	M	A	B	M
−82.5°	0	0	1	0	0	1	0	.2	.8	0	.4	.6
−67.5°	.2	.2	.68	.2	0	.8	.2	0	.8	.2	.2	.68
−52.5°	.4	.4	.52	.4	.2	.56	.4	0	.6	.4	0	.6
−37.5°	.6	.6	.52	.6	.4	.48	.6	.2	.44	.6	0	.4
−22.5°	.8	.8	.68	.8	.6	.56	.8	.4	.44	.8	.2	.32
−7.5°	1	1	1	1	.8	.8	1	.6	.6	1	.4	.4
7.5°	1	1	1	1	1	1	1	.8	.8	1	.6	.6
22.5°	.8	.8	.68	.8	1	.8	.8	1	.8	.8	.8	.68
37.5°	.6	.6	.52	.6	.8	.56	.6	1	.6	.6	1	.6
52.5°	.4	.4	.52	.4	.6	.48	.4	.8	.44	.4	1	.4
67.5°	.2	.2	.68	.2	.4	.56	.2	.6	.44	.2	.8	.32
82.5°	0	0	1	0	.2	.8	0	.4	.6	0	.6	.4
	M totals 8.8			8.4			7.36			6.0		

Polariz. angle, ϕ	60°			75°			90°		
	A	B	M	A	B	M	A	B	M
−82.5°	0	.6	.4	0	.8	.2	0	1	0
−67.5°	.2	.4	.56	.2	.6	.44	.2	.8	.32
−52.5°	.4	.2	.56	.4	.4	.52	.4	.6	.48
−37.5°	.6	0	.4	.6	.2	.44	.6	.4	.48
−22.5°	.8	0	.2	.8	0	.2	.8	.2	.32
−7.5°	1	.2	.2	1	0	0	1	0	0
7.5°	1	.4	.4	1	.2	.2	1	0	0
22.5°	.8	.6	.56	.8	.4	.44	.8	.2	.32
37.5°	.6	.8	.56	.6	.6	.52	.6	.4	.48
52.5°	.4	1	.4	.4	.8	.44	.4	.6	.48
67.5°	.2	1	.2	.2	1	.2	.2	.8	.32
82.5°	0	.8	.2	0	1	0	0	1	0
	M totals 4.64			3.6			3.2		

What should be the reading, M, of the coincidence counter? Assuming that the path followed by each photon is *independent* of that of its twin, the probabilities can be multiplied to give the joint probability

$$M = AB + (1 - A)(1 - B).$$

The probability of getting no match (0,1 or 1,0) is given by

$$p_{nomatch} = A(1 - B) + B(1 - A).$$

Since $M + p_{nomatch}$ has to equal 1, as a check, the sum of the right-hand sides of the above equations yields 1.

The format of Table 6-2 is identical to that of Table 6-1. The B column rotates down one row distance, $\phi = 15°$, as we move to the right one column distance, $\theta = 15°$. The M totals are plotted, versus θ, in Fig. 6-2(b).

There is no question but that this curve, which is based on Table 6-2, is shaped like the experimentally measured $\cos^2\theta$ curve of Fig. 6-2(a). It looks as if the conjecture accurately describes the measured curve. Nevertheless, there are two serious objections to the new curve. First, the derivation assumes that "the path followed by each photon is independent of that of its twin." Since the two photons have highly correlated, in fact identical, polarization angles, it may be dangerous to assume that their path choices are uncorrelated. Second, the curve of Table 6-2 has a large displacement from the $M = 0$ baseline; the minimum value, at $\theta = 90°$, is given by $M_{total} = 3.2$. For the curves of Fig. 6-2(a), on the other hand, the minimum value is zero for both the expected and measured curves. [Notice that the vertical scale in Fig. 6-2(b) starts at $M = 2$, and is magnified 2-to-1 compared to that of (a).]

Because of the above objections, it seems to me that the explanation offered by Fig. 6-3 is more reasonable than that of Fig. 6-2(b). Both figures, however, may contribute to the conjecture that can solve the mystery behind Bell's theorem.

6-5. Experiment Using Interferometers

This chapter ends with a second experimental setup that is very similar to that of Fig. 6-1. It is depicted in Fig. 6-4. Some of the following discussion is a paraphrase of that concerning Fig. 6-1.

The central block is a twin-state photon generator. In the apparatus described by Raymond Y. Chiao et al. (1993), the generator is a "spontaneous

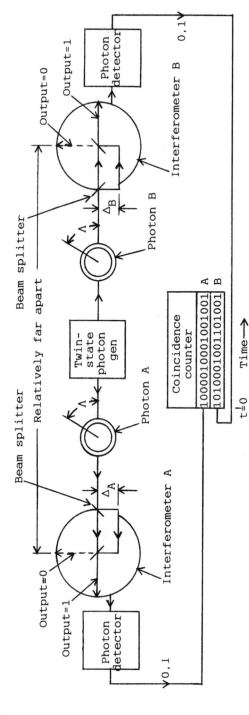

Fig. 6-4. A second experiment from which it is concluded that photons *A* and *B* somehow communicate with each other superluminally. Some characteristic, *Λ*,
is the same for both photons. Each photon strikes a beam splitter; with equal
probability, the photon proceeds to (1) a second beam splitter (at the center
of the interferometer circle), or (2) it is reflected to a path that is longer by
manually-adjustable 2Δ$_A$ on the left, and 2Δ$_B$ on the right. At the second
beam splitter, each photon exits the interferometer along the 1 output path,
or along the 0 output path.

parametric down-conversion crystal." It has nonlinear optical properties. When a single ultraviolet photon ($f \cong 8 \times 10^{14}$ Hz) strikes the crystal, it is converted down in frequency into two infrared photons ($f \cong 4 \times 10^{14}$ Hz). The latter have somewhat different frequencies, in general, but the sum of their frequencies equals that of the parent photon. (In accordance with $E_{ph} = fh$, therefore, photon energy is conserved.)

We again will have a situation in which the left photon seems to know how the right photon will behave and vice versa. We again remark that the photons seem to communicate with each other superluminally. How is this possible?

The photons seem to share a particular characteristic, which I call Λ. In Fig. 6-4, for want of a more convenient way to display Λ, it is shown like the polarization angles of Fig. 6-1. However, Λ is *not* a polarization angle (although the polarization angle may contribute to Λ). Furthermore, the experiment of Fig. 6-4 does not measure the polarization angle.

What it does measure and compare are the paths taken by the A and B twin photons when they travel through interferometers A on the left and B on the right, respectively.

Each photon first strikes a beam splitter, which is analogous to an imperfect mirror: If illuminated by a laser beam, about half of the photons that strike the splitter are allowed to pass through, but the other half are subjected to mirror-type reflection into the path that is longer by $2\Delta_A$ in the left interferometer, or $2\Delta_B$ in the right. (To simplify the drawing, corner mirror reflectors are not shown.)

It is possible to manually adjust Δ_A and Δ_B. In what follows, the pathlength difference, 2Δ, is equal to $2(\Delta_B - \Delta_A)$. (This is analogous to $\theta = \theta_B - \theta_A$ in Fig. 6-1.) Also, in what follows, it is convenient to refer only to the left half of Fig. 6-4, but the discussion applies equally well to the right half.

To change the path length by a full wavelength, $2\Delta_A$ has to approximately change a distance equal to $c/f \cong 3 \times 10^8/4 \times 10^{14} \cong 750$ nm. Normally, a range of ¼ wavelength is sufficient, or a Δ_A change of 100 nm = 1000 Å. This is minuscule (a water molecule has a diameter of 3 Å), but it is feasible and easily controlled in a design that uses piezoelectric transducers.

We now have an interferometer: A laser beam strikes the beam splitter; half of its photons take the short path to the center of the A interferometer in Fig. 6-4, and the other half take the longer path whose length can be altered by changing Δ_A. The two beams come together in the center of the circle. Remember that each beam consists of a sinusoidal EMF wave.

If Δ_A is adjusted so that the sine waves representing each beam are in phase, we have constructive interference; if Δ_A is set so that the sine waves representing each beam cancel, we have destructive interference. In the latter event, what happens to the energy conveyed by the sine waves (which can be quite high)? The answer is that, in Fig. 6-4, the beams approach each other at right angles, so the effects of destructive and constructive interference spatially alternate. Peaks and valleys form exactly as in Fig. 3-3(c), and the energy follows the constructive interference pathways. Even if we could arrange to have parallel beams, they could not possibly be plane EMFs everywhere; at the edges of each beam, destructive and constructive interference effects would, again, spatially alternate, forming peaks and valleys.

But let us not digress into laser beams. We should be concerned here with a pair of *single, isolated* photons. When the photon arrives at the first beam splitter, the wave-particle duality (WPD) field splits, one segment proceeding to the center of the interferometer circle, the other reflected into the longer path. With equal probability the power pack sometimes chooses the shorter path, sometimes the Δ-modulated path. Where the two paths meet, at the center of the circle, we get various degrees of constructive and destructive interference, depending on the setting of Δ_A.

Incidentally, this suggests a way to measure the putative WPD fields. As the path-length difference $2\Delta_A$ increases, we expect to see a decrease in the amplitude of the interference effect. This is probably not a clear-cut experiment if the two beams meet at right angles, but it should be possible to use mirrors to deflect each beam through 45°, say, so that they are parallel when they come together.

In Fig. 6-1, each calcite filter provides two quadrature polarizations: a 1 output (solid line), and a 0 output (dashed line). An exactly analogous setup is followed in Fig. 6-4. At the center of each interferometer circle, a second beam splitter directs the emergent beam (or photon, in our case) either to a 1 output (solid line) or a 0 output (dashed line).

As before, the photon outputs, 1 or 0, are detected by photomultipliers, and outputs of the "photon detector" blocks are compared in a coincidence counter.

In Fig. 6-1, the photons' polarization angle ϕ is a random variable. To check for correlation between the left and right photons, we change the calcite filter difference angle, θ. In Fig. 6-4, the random variable is the path taken by the photon's power pack: At the first beam splitter, will it take the direct path or the Δ-modulated path? At the second beam splitter, will it exit along the 1 line or along the 0 line? To check for correlation between the left and right photons, we change the path length difference, $2\Delta = 2(\Delta_B - \Delta_A)$, by varying Δ_A and/or Δ_B.

What are the experimental results? They are similar to those of Fig. 6-2(a) if we replace θ by the path length difference, 2Δ. For relatively small values of 2Δ, the correlation is greater than expected.

I offer the conjecture of Fig. 6-3(b) as an explanation. Interaction between (a) the photon's power pack and/or its compression shock wave, and (b) the ether streamlines, are able to slightly change the power pack's time of arrival, perhaps by causing it to spiral or wobble or zigzag along its path. This would be equivalent to changing the path-length difference, 2Δ. What I am leading up to, of course, is that these random Δ changes correspond to the random ϕ shifts of Fig. 6-3. The conjecture is that the interaction between photons and the mirrors and/or the putative ether is characterized by small random ϕ shifts.

The main point is that small, random perturbations in the photons' path length can approximate the $\cos^2\theta$ function, and "this leads to the false and impossible conclusion that the twin photons are instantaneously communicating with each other so as to obtain greater than expected correlation, or probability of matches," for relatively small values of Δ.

Chapter 7

Special Relativity

7-1. Some Principles of Special Relativity

Albert Einstein published his theory of special relativity in 1905 [A. P. French, 1968; W. Rindler, 1982]. One of the tenets of the special theory is that the luminiferous (light-transmitting) ether—a mysterious substance that was postulated to fill all of vacuum space—does not exist. In this chapter, however, we sometimes find justification for the thesis that the universe is filled with this mysterious substance. Since this is a conjecture, it legitimizes the inclusion of this chapter in the book. (Unfortunately, some people will interpret this in a negative manner.)

We now know that the atom is almost completely "empty space" because the volume occupied by electrons, protons, and neutrons is minuscule. The universe, in the present chapter, therefore consists of tiny displacements, here and there, by a particle that has mass (a "massive" particle), surrounded by a huge volume of empty space that is either a vacuum or filled with "ether," crisscrossed here and there by speeding photon wave packets.

Another tenet of the special theory of relativity is that the speed of light (electromagnetic field, or EMF propagation) is everywhere constant. As measured on the earth it is, of course, $c = 2.998 \times 10^8$ meters/second in a vacuum. (From here on in this chapter, because c is used over and over again, it will be more convenient to use $c = 3 \times 10^8$ m/s.) On a quasar that is receding from the earth at a speed of $0.8c$, or 2.4×10^8 m/s (150,000 miles/second), c is measured to be 3×10^8 m/s. On some distant earth that is approaching our earth at a speed of $0.6c$ (110,000 miles/s), EMF propagation in a vacuum is at 3×10^8 m/s, and so forth.

All of the above measurements are made in an "inertial reference frame"; that is, by a stationary observer in a laboratory that is moving through space in a straight line, not speeding up or slowing down; it is not accelerating. The earth is an imperfect inertial reference frame: First, because the earth is rotating on its axis within a period of 24 hours, we are accelerating toward the center of the earth, and rely on gravity to keep us from flying off at a tangent (but the centrifugal force is a negligible component of your weight on a scale). Second, because the earth is rotating around the sun within a period of approximately 365 days, we constantly experience a radial acceleration toward the sun. The gravitational attraction between the sun and earth is responsible for the radial acceleration that, fortunately, keeps the earth in an approximately circular orbit, at around 30,000 meters/second, rather than letting it fly off into space along a straight line. Third, the moon also has an acceleration effect, as is evidenced by the tides. Nevertheless, these three components (and others) of the earth's acceleration are relatively weak forces, negligible for almost all purposes, so we can assume that a stationary observer on earth is in an inertial reference frame.

Still another tenet of the special theory of relativity is that any object having mass (here I primarily mean the electron, proton, or neutron) cannot exceed the speed of light (as measured, of course, by a stationary observer in the inertial reference frame). In the above examples, therefore, it would be incorrect to speak of a quasar that is receding from us at a speed of, say, $1.2c$ (the maximum thus far observed is around $0.95c$). Similarly, it would be impossible for some distant earth to approach us at a speed of $1.2c$.

The mysterious ether became even more of an enigma in 1887 when Albert A. Michelson (1852–1931) and Edward W. Morley (1838–1923) set up their famous experiment. It was analogous to measuring the speed of a boat going downstream, across stream, and upstream. For a boat, of course, the downstream speed is $v_0 + v$, where v_0 is the boat's speed in still water, and v is the velocity of the stream. Going upstream the speed is $v_0 - v$. (As usual, speed is measured relative to a "stationary observer.")

Michelson-Morley assumed that the earth is moving relative to the ether, like a boat in a stream. They proceeded to measure the velocity of light downstream, across stream, and upstream. Their apparatus was sensitive enough to respond to the difference between the speeds of the earth as it rotates on its axis and around the sun, and that of light. For their experiment, in other words, 30,000 m/s *was* an appreciable speed. Their result was always the same—the speed of light is independent of the ether. It was as if the ether was moving *with* the earth, or at least with the prestigious Michelson-Morley laboratory. This sounds as unscientific as the ancient notion that the universe is rotating around an omnipotent earth.

Einstein's theory of special relativity dealt a fatal blow to the ether. Why should we concern ourselves with the speed of the ether with respect to the earth, or with respect to any other nonaccelerating observer, if the velocity of the EMF is everywhere 3×10^8 m/s? Everywhere includes the earth, or a receding quasar, or an approaching star. We do not know what electric and magnetic fields really are, but they are somehow able to propagate in a true vacuum, without the need for a luminiferous ether. Since 1905, the ether has simply been ignored.

Well, not completely. I soon discovered, in looking for the "ether" in indexes, that it is sometimes spelled "aether." This is the way Edmund T. Whittaker (1951) and P. J. E. Peebles (1993) spell it, which makes much more sense than the homonymous ether that is used as an anesthetic. In the present book I use "ether," because that seems to be the popular spelling [L. S. Swenson, Jr., 1972], although either is correct.

7-2. The Lorentz Contraction

The situation is much more complicated than the mere dismissal of the ether as a contentious substance. Following the Michelson-Morley experiment, Hendrik A. Lorentz (1853–1928) and George F. FitzGerald (1851–1901), around 1892, explained the unexpected results *without regard to the ether.* They proposed that an object moving with respect to the stationary observer becomes shortened, or contracted, along the direction to the observer, as seen by the observer. The contraction is the same regardless of whether the object is receding or approaching. This came to be known as the Lorentz contraction. It is one of the greatest intellectual achievements of all time because it implies that space can be curved, and that time can be different to different nonaccelerating observers.

The above is illustrated in Fig. 7-1, which is based on the Michelson-Morley experiment. In (a) we have an L-shaped structure; the length of each leg is 0.12 meter. At the end of each leg is a mirror, as shown. At time

$t = 0$, the structure is stationary with respect to a nonaccelerating observer at the lower-left corner. The idea is that the observer simultaneously launches light beams that are directed to each mirror. [The vertical beam is not shown in (a).] Both beams return from the mirrors simultaneously, of course. Since the roundtrip distance is 0.24 m, the roundtrip time is

$$\frac{0.24 \text{ m}}{3 \times 10^8 \text{ m/s}} = 0.8 \times 10^{-9} \text{ second} = 0.8 \text{ nanosecond.}$$

(Nanosecond time intervals are easily measured with sophisticated electronic equipment.)

At $t = 0^+$, following a heroic stretch of the imagination, three changes take place ($t = 0^+$ is a shorthand way of indicating an infinitesimal time after $t = 0$):

1. The L-shaped structure starts to move to the right at a *constant* velocity of 0.6c, or 1.8×10^8 m/s.

2. Because of the tremendous horizontal velocity, the beam that was originally launched vertically now has to be fired off at an angle of elevation of 53.13°, as shown, in order to properly meet its mirror.

3. Again, because of the tremendous horizontal velocity, there is an appreciable Lorentz contraction. The horizontal leg shortens by a factor of $\gamma = 1.25$, to a length of 0.096 m, as shown. The vertical leg retains its original length of 0.12 m because there is no motion in this direction.

It usually is sloppy bookkeeping, and a regrettable source of confusion, if an author uses the same symbol for two different parameters. Here γ is the Lorentz contraction factor and, in Chap. 4, γ is the relativistic increase in mass factor, the increase in effective mass due to speed. Well, it turns out that the *same* γ is correct in these two different definitions. This is surely not a coincidence.

If my Lorentz contraction calculation is correct, the two simultaneously launched beams will simultaneously arrive at the lower-left corner of the L, thus verifying that the velocity of light is 3×10^8 m/s along each path despite the fact that one path was (at rest) much longer than the other.

Next, consider the "motion-picture" frames (b) to (e):

Fig. 7-1(b): $t = 0.25$ ns. The L has moved 0.045 m to the right. Each light beam has traveled 0.075 m from its starting point.

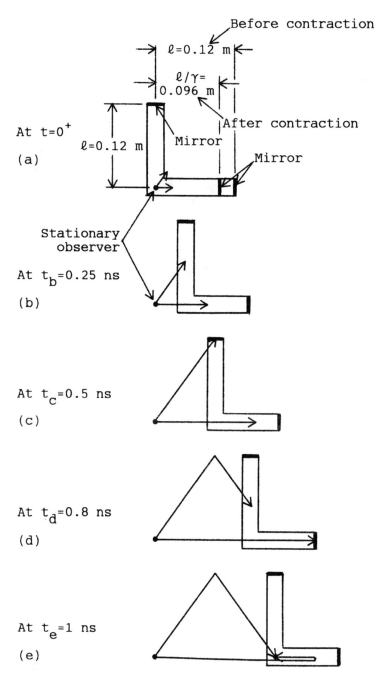

Fig. 7-1. Numerical example that uses the Lorentz contraction to illustrate that the velocity of light is constant as measured by a stationary observer. (a)At $t = 0^+$, the L-shaped structure starts to move to the right at a velocity of 1.8×10^8 m/s; the observer launches two light beams; the horizontal leg contracts from 0.12 to 0.096 m. (b)At $t = 0.25$ ns. (c)At $t = 0.5$ ns, the "53°" beam has reached its mirror. (d)At $t = 0.8$ ns, the horizontal beam has reached its mirror. (e)At $t = 1$ ns, both beams simultaneously return to the starting point on the L.

Fig. 7-1(c): $t = 0.5$ ns. The L has moved 0.09 m to the right. Each beam has traveled $vt = (3 \times 10^8)(0.5 \times 10^{-9}) = 0.15$ m. This is exactly the correct amount for the 53° beam to meet its mirror. It starts its downward flight.

Fig. 7-1(d): $t = 0.8$ ns. The L has moved 0.144 m to the right. Each beam has traveled 0.24 m. This is exactly the correct amount for the horizontal beam to meet its mirror, since 0.144 m plus the leg length of 0.096 m equals 0.24 m. The horizontal beam starts its leftward return flight.

Fig. 7-1(e): $t = 1$ ns. The L has moved 0.18 m to the right. Each beam has traveled 0.3 m. This is exactly the correct amount for the 53° beam to arrive at the lower-left corner, because each leg of its triangle is 0.15 m long. At the same time, the horizontal beam arrives at the lower-left corner because the 0.24 m travel of (d), minus the return segment of 0.06 m in 0.2 ns, equals 0.18 m.

It is a simple, if not rigorous, matter to derive the equations related to special relativity from Fig. 7-1. Each leg of the L has an original length ℓ, and it moves to the right with a velocity v. The all-important Lorentz contraction factor turns out to be

$$ \gamma = \frac{1}{[1 - (v/c)^2]^{1/2}}. $$

For the numerical values in Fig. 7-1, where $v = 0.6c$, we verify that $\gamma = 1.25$. Notice that γ is always equal to or greater than 1.

There are several deep philosophical questions associated with Fig. 7-1:

Does the Lorentz contraction really occur? The evidence is that it does, and the velocity of the EMF is always, everywhere, 3×10^8 m/s in a vacuum.

What causes the contraction? What mechanism can explain the shrinkage, by a factor of 1.25, if $v = 0.6c$? The effect is analogous to the compression of an elastic body, caused by viscosity, as it moves through a liquid or gas. The contraction is independent of the direction, just as the roundtrip for a boat going upstream and then downstream is the same as for the reverse sequence.

Furthermore, as pointed out above, for a given velocity v, the contraction factor γ in the direction of motion is exactly the same as the effective increase in mass!

But if we resuscitate the ether we have to also restore the notion that every massive body has its own ether. The earth's ether moves with the earth; the sun's ether is stationary with respect to the sun and, similarly,

every planet and star and quasar is immersed in its own, relatively stationary, ether.

Furthermore, space can be curved. In Fig. 7-1, obviously, the horizontal contraction without a corresponding vertical contraction can only be
accomplished by squeezing or bending the structure. This is commonly
known as the "warping" of space.

7-3. Time Dilation

The most amazing result of the Lorentz contraction, one that excites the
imagination with its promise of everlasting (if suspended) life, is the dilation of time. In Fig. 7-1, the stationary observer's watch reading, and the
aging that he or she undergoes, is different from that of a person moving
with the horizontal arm, as follows:

The nonaccelerating, stationary observer measures the time taken for
the beam to traverse an arm. When the L is stationary, the time is

$$\frac{0.12 \text{ m}}{3 \times 10^8 \text{ m/s}} = 0.4 \text{ ns.}$$

When the L is moving, however, the time to traverse the horizontal arm (as
seen by the stationary observer) is

$$\frac{0.096 \text{ m}}{3 \times 10^8 \text{ m/s}} = 0.32 \text{ ns.}$$

To an observer moving with the arm, it remains 0.12 m long because this
observer's ruler shrinks along with the arm.

The implication is that, in general, a clock moving with velocity v
(through the ether?) is slowed down by a factor γ. If it is a pendulum clock,
the period increases (hence the expression, time dilation) as seen by a stationary (with respect to the ether?) observer. The standard scenario shows
a space ship that travels at a tremendous speed away from the earth, somehow reverses course, and returns at a tremendous speed. Both ways, going
and coming, the people aboard the space ship age less than those left behind on earth. Imagine returning to earth younger than your children! (Believe it or not, a good portion of the pages of the "Skeptical Inquirer" are
devoted to deprecating scientifically illiterate individuals who, ignorant of
the huge amount of necessary energy, routinely launch flying saucers into
outer space.)

A discrepancy surfaces here, and it is reviewed in Fig. 7-2. A space vehicle leaves the earth, accelerates to a speed of 1.8×10^8 m/s, and maintains this speed constant from x_A to x_B, a distance of 180 m. At x_B the vehicle undergoes centrifugal acceleration (that is, it follows a circular path) without changing speed. The speed remains constant at 1.8×10^8 m/s from x_B to x_A. Then the vehicle decelerates, landing smoothly at the Earth Airport. An earth clock shows that

$$t_{AB} + t_{BA} = \frac{360 \text{ meters}}{1.8 \times 10^8 \text{ m/s}} = 2 \text{ microseconds} = 2 \ \mu s.$$

At the same time, a homunculus aboard the space vehicle, reading the vehicle's clock, indicates that

$$t_{AB} + t_{BA} = 1.6 \ \mu s$$

because, at the vehicle's speed, $\gamma = 1.25$. In other words, the space vehicle only ages 1.6 μs while the earth ages 2 μs.

During the trip, however, the homunculus looked back at the earth and this is what he or she saw: Relative to the space vehicle, from x_A to x_B, the

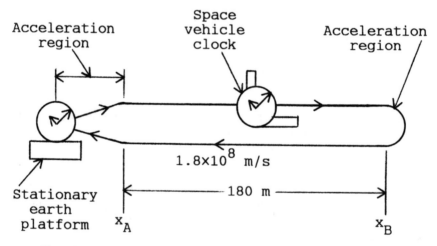

Fig. 7-2. Illustrating a discrepancy that arises because, during constant motion between x_A and x_B, the earth may appear to be moving relative to a stationary space vehicle, rather than the other way around. A homunculus on the space vehicle ages 1.6 μs if he or she is moving, but 2 μs if the earth is moving. The discrepancy is absorbed if the time periods of acceleration (and deceleration) are included, leaving the homunculus aging 0.4 μs less than the earth.

earth retreated at a speed of 1.8×10^8 m/s, and then returned at the same speed. The vehicle's clock should accordingly show

$$t_{BA} + t_{AB} = \frac{360}{1.8 \times 10^8} = 2 \, \mu s.$$

The discrepancy arises because we have neglected clock readings during the two acceleration regions. There *is* a difference between the earth and the space vehicle: the earth never accelerates, but the space vehicle goes through periods of tremendous acceleration (and deceleration). If the latter time periods are included, we should find that the $t_{vehicle}$ discrepancy disappears, and the homunculus's clock reading ends up as $0.4 \, \mu s$ less than that of the earth's clock. Thus, people on the space vehicle age less than those on earth.

On this subject, I highly recommend Chap. 2, "Clocks, Rulers, and the Universal Speed Limit" in Mills (1994). However, the topic of human differential aging because of space flight should not be taken seriously because of the enormous energy required to accelerate to the velocity at which an appreciable effect occurs. Relative to our home base, the earth, we have to be dreaming about a velocity of 1×10^8 m/s (60,000 miles per *second*).

There may be a problem in observing a distant quasar. If it is receding from us with velocity v, which includes the ether in which it is embedded, the integrated billions of light years between the earth and the quasar must bear the imprint of that relative velocity v, and the photons that reach us must show the equivalent of time dilation. These effects become appreciable when $v/c \cong 0.3$, which corresponds to $\gamma = 1.05$. The most distant quasars show $v/c \cong 0.95$, which corresponds to $\gamma = 3$. Quasar time dilation is considered, below, in a numerical example.

7-4. Conventional Doppler Shift

All of the information we have about quasars is based, of course, on the photons that have survived the unbelievably vast expanse of space and time. Their spectra show a decreasing frequency, or shift towards the red end (and beyond) of the visible spectrum. The shift is a gradually increasing function of distance from the earth. This is interpreted as evidence that the universe is expanding (the quasars are moving away from us). The spectral shift includes a "relativistic" shift because of the time dilation factor, γ. This is further explained in Section 7-5.

First, in the present section, consider the conventional Doppler shift: This is commonly noticed in connection with changes in sound frequency as a generator (sound source) moves toward or away from us. A numerical example is depicted, in Fig. 7-3.

In (a) we have a stationary receiver at $x = 0$ and, at $t = 0$, a 5-Hz generator located 200 m to the right of the receiver. Sound propagates at a velocity of 1000 m/s through the medium. At $t = 0$, the generator simultaneously launches the 5-Hz signal and it starts to move to the right with a constant velocity of 800 m/s. A 1–s interval is illustrated.

Although the analysis of conventional Doppler would seem to be trivial, it has pitfalls. Students tend to confuse spatial waveforms with time waveforms. It is logical to derive first the *spatial* waveforms, as in (b), and from these the time waveforms, as in (c).

To derive the spatial waveforms of (b), first select a reasonable horizontal distance scale, with $x = 0$ underneath the $x = 0$ of (a). The horizontal scale is calibrated in meters. Next, draw a triangle as shown, with $t = 0$ underneath the $t = 0$ of (a). The rows inside the triangle are "photographs" taken at one-cycle intervals; that is, at $t = 0, 0.2, 0.4, \ldots, 1$ s. The left edge of the triangle represents the leading edge of the 5-Hz wave as it propagates to the left at 1000 m/s. The right edge represents the generator as it moves to the right at 800 m/s.

The vertical column of dots at $x = 0$, in (b), reveals the waveform seen by the receiver. These dots are plotted in (c), using a horizontal scale that is calibrated in seconds, to depict the received waveform. Its frequency is 2.778 Hz (there is one cycle every 0.36 s). In this case, therefore, the received frequency is less than the generator frequency.

The received frequency is, in general, given by

$$f_r = \frac{f_0}{1 + (v/v_s)},$$

where f_r = received (shifted) frequency,

$\quad$ f_0 = generator frequency,

$\quad\quad$ v = generator velocity *going away* from the stationary receiver,

$\quad\quad$ v_s = velocity of sound propagation.

For Fig. 7-3, the equation immediately gives $f_r = 5/1.8 = 2.778$ Hz. If the generator is moving toward the receiver, v becomes negative, the denominator becomes less than 1, so the received frequency is greater than the generator frequency.

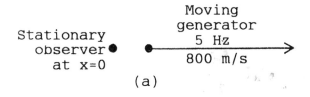

(a)

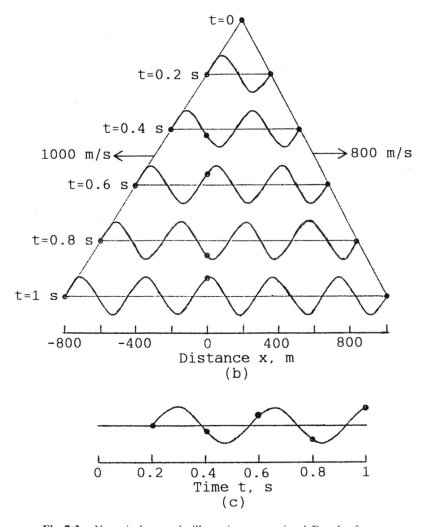

Fig. 7-3.   Numerical example illustrating conventional Doppler frequency shift caused by a receding generator. (a)The physical setup. (b)Spatial waveforms of 5-Hz signal at $t = 0, 0.2$ s, 0.4 s, . . . , 1 s. Sound velocity in the medium is 1000 m/s, while the generator recedes at a velocity of 800 m/s. Dots are used to emphasize the signal received by the observer at $x = 0$. (c)Time waveform, at $x = 0$, derived from (b). The received frequency is 2.778 Hz.

7-5. Relativistic Doppler Shift

For light emitted by a quasar, besides the conventional Doppler f_r shift, we have an additional shift factor because of time dilation. Dividing by γ, we get

$$f_r = f_0 \left[\frac{1 - (v/c)}{1 + (v/c)} \right]^{1/2} .$$

Notice that this accommodates equally well receding (positive-v) or approaching (negative-v) generators.

Cosmologists find f_r/f_0 to be unnatural because it becomes smaller as the shift toward lower frequency—the red shift—becomes more pronounced. Therefore, they prefer to use the redshift z defined as

$$z = \frac{f_0}{f_r} - 1.$$

If there is no relative motion, $f_0 = f_r$ and $z = 0$. As the recession velocity increases, however, z increases.

Some numerical values are given, in Table 7-1, as a function of v/v_s or v/c. The second column gives the conventional Doppler shift. The third column lists the relativistic shift that includes time dilation. The last two columns show conventional and relativistic shifts, respectively, if the generator is *approaching* the earth so that v is negative. These are also known as blue shifts.

Figure 7-3 illustrates the $v/v_s = 0.8$ row of Table 7-1, where the conventional Doppler shift is $f_r/f_0 = 0.5556$. It may be interesting and informative to show how this figure changes if v/c remains at 0.8 and the drawing is modified to include time dilation. To use the same curves as those of Fig. 7-3, the following values are used for Fig. 7-4.

In (a) we have a stationary nonaccelerating receiver at $x = 0$ and, at $t = 0$, a 5-Hz generator located 0.6×10^8 m to the right of the receiver. (I realize that 5 Hz is a super-low frequency, but it allows me to use the curves of Fig. 7-3.) The 5-Hz EMF wave propagates at its usual velocity of 3×10^8 m/s. At $t = 0$, the generator simultaneously launches the 5-Hz signal and it starts to move to the right with a constant velocity of 2.4×10^8 m/s.

Here is how time dilation manifests itself: In Fig. 7-3, the rows of (b) are "photographs" taken at one-cycle intervals. In Fig. 7-4, however, all time values are multiplied by γ, but the distance values remain as for conventional Doppler. In (b), since $\gamma = 1.667$, the rows are "photographs" taken at $t = 0, 0.3333, 0.6667, \ldots , 1.667$ s. As before, the vertical column

Table 7-1. Various values of velocity ratio v/v_s (for sound) or v/c (for EMFs) versus their Doppler shifts f_r/f_0. Columns 2 and 3 list conventional (sound) and relativistic (EMF) Doppler, respectively. z is the redshift characteristic, and γ is the Lorentz contraction (and time dilation) factor. The last two columns are for negative (approaching) velocity ratios.

Veloc. ratio v/v_s or v/c	Receding Doppler ratio f_r/f_0		Redshift z	Contraction factor γ	Approach Doppler ratio f_r/f_0	
	Conventional	Relativistic			Conventional	Relativistic
0	1	1	0	1	1	1
0.1	0.9091	0.9045	0.1055	1.005	1.111	1.106
0.2	0.8333	0.8165	0.2247	1.021	1.250	1.225
0.3	0.7692	0.7338	0.3628	1.048	1.429	1.363
0.4	0.7143	0.6547	0.5275	1.091	1.667	1.528
0.5	0.6667	0.5774	0.7321	1.155	2	1.732
0.6	0.6250	0.5	1	1.250	2.5	2
0.7	0.5882	0.4201	1.380	1.400	3.333	2.380
0.8	0.5556	0.3333	2	1.667	5	3
0.9	0.5263	0.2294	3.359	2.294	10	4.359
1	0.5	0	∞	∞	∞	∞

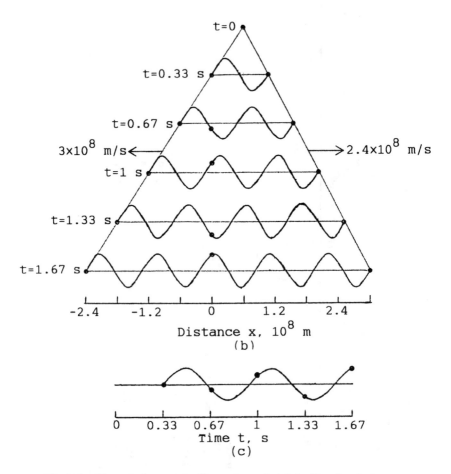

Fig. 7-4. Numerical example illustrating relativistic Doppler frequency shift caused by a receding generator. (a)The physical setup. (b)Spatial waveforms of 5-Hz signal at $t = 0$, 0.33 s, 0.67 s, . . . , 1.67 s. EMF velocity is 3×10^8 m/s, while the generator recedes at a velocity of 2.4×10^8 m/s. Dots are used to emphasize the signal received by the observer at $x = 0$. (c)Time waveform, at $x = 0$, derived from (b). The received frequency is 1.667 Hz.

of dots at $x = 0$, in (b), reveals the waveform seen by the receiver in (c). Its frequency is 1.667 Hz (there is one cycle every 0.6 s). The relativistic Doppler shift ratio, $f_r/f_0 = 1.667/5 = 0.3333$, agrees with the $v/c = 0.8$ row of Table 7-1.

The conjecture is that much of this comes about because the quasar is immersed in its own ether, which is receding relative to the earth's ether.

7-6. Doppler Shifts of Approaching Generators

The chapter ends with examples in which the generator is approaching the stationary receiver. First, conventional sound Doppler is depicted in Fig. 7-5.

In (a) we have the receiver at $x = 0$ and, at $t = 0$, a 5-Hz generator located 800 m to the right of the receiver. Sound propagates at a velocity of 1000 m/s through the medium. At $t = 0$, the generator simultaneously launches the 5-Hz signal and it starts to move to the left with a constant velocity of 600 m/s. A 1-s interval is illustrated.

To derive the spatial waveforms of (b), as in Figs. 7-3 and 7-4, first select a reasonable horizontal distance scale, with $x = 0$ underneath the $x = 0$ of (a). Next, draw a triangle as shown, with $t = 0$ underneath the $t = 0$ of (a). The rows inside the triangle are "photographs" taken at one-cycle intervals; that is, at $t = 0$, 0.2, 0.4, . . . , 1 s. The left edge of the triangle represents the leading edge of the 5-Hz wave as it propagates to the left at 1000 m/s. The right edge represents the generator as it moves to the left at 600 m/s.

The waveform seen by the receiver at $x = 0$ is plotted in (c). The frequency is 12.5 Hz (there is one cycle every 0.08 s). The Doppler shift ratio, $f_r/f_0 = 12.5/5 = 2.5$, agrees with the $v/v_s = 0.6$ row of Table 7-1.

Finally, consider an example of relativistic Doppler in Fig. 7-6, retaining the curves of Fig. 7-5 with $v/c = 0.6$.

In (a) we have a stationary receiver at $x = 0$ and, at $t = 0$, a 5-Hz generator located 2.4×10^8 m to the right of the receiver. The 5-Hz EMF propagates at a velocity of 3×10^8 m/s. At $t = 0$, the generator simultaneously launches the 5-Hz signal and it starts to move to the left with a constant velocity of 1.8×10^8 m/s.

In Fig. 7-5, the rows of (b) are "photographs" taken at one-cycle intervals. In Fig. 7-6, however, because of time dilation, all time values are multiplied by γ, but distance values remain as for conventional Doppler.

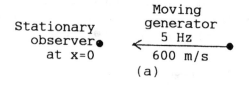

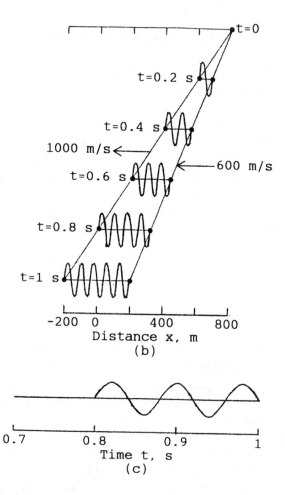

Fig. 7-5. Numerical example illustrating conventional Doppler frequency
shift caused by an approaching generator. (a)The physical setup.
(b)Spatial waveforms of 5-Hz signal at $t = 0, 0.2$ s, 0.4 s, . . . , 1 s.
Sound velocity in the medium is 1000 m/s, while the generator approaches at a velocity of 600 m/s. (c)Time waveform, at $x = 0$, derived from (b). The received frequency is 12.5 Hz.

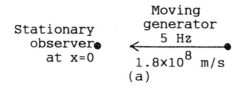

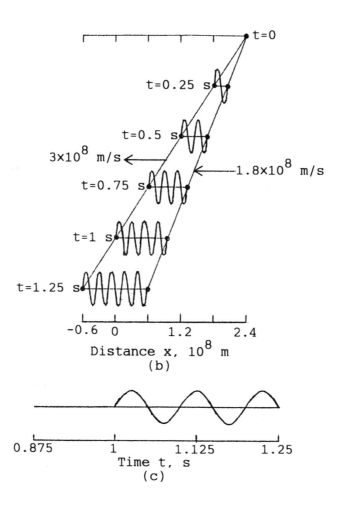

Fig. 7-6. Numerical example illustrating relativistic Doppler frequency
shift caused by an approaching generator: (a)The physical setup.
(b)Spatial waveforms of 5-Hz signal at $t = 0$, 0.25 s, 0.5 s, . . . ,
1.25 s. EMF velocity is 3×10^8 m/s, while the generator approaches at a velocity of 1.8×10^8 m/s. (c)Time waveform, at
$x = 0$, derived from (b). The received frequency is 10 Hz.

In (b), since $\gamma = 1.25$, the rows are "photographs" taken at $t = 0, 0.25, 0.5,$ ..., 1.25 s. The waveform seen by the receiver at $x = 0$ is plotted in (c). The frequency is 10 Hz (there is one cycle every 0.1 s). The Doppler shift ratio, $f_r/f_0 = 10/5 = 2$, agrees with the $v/c = 0.6$ row of Table 7-1.

I can only repeat my cosmological argument for the restoration of the ether. It can provide an explanation for the flattening, space warping, and time dilation that occur when a material object moves toward or away from us at relativistic speeds (greater than $0.3c$, or greater than 1×10^8 m/s).

The weak signal we receive from a distant quasar consists of individual photons, minuscule wave packets such as that of Fig. 1-1, and not the plane EMF waves of Fig. 3-2. When a photon leaves a quasar that is receding from us, the photon's velocity has to subsequently increase, as it traverses intergalactic space, to the value it has when it strikes the earth, 3×10^8 m/s. How does it "know" when to increase its velocity? Why should its velocity increase? Perhaps the medium changes, from a receding ether to the one in which our galaxy is embedded.

Chapter 8

Model of the Universe

8-1. The Big Bang

This chapter is concerned with cosmology—the study of the origins, dynamics, and structure of the universe. Much of the material is based on a remarkable book, *Principles of Physical Cosmology,* by Phillip J. E. Peebles (1993). The book is remarkable because it is more than 720 pages long, filled with equations, tables, and illustrations as well as text. One should also refer to *The Nature of Space and Time,* by Stephen W. Hawking and Roger Penrose (1996), and to *Cosmology and Controversy: The Historical Development of Two Theories of the Universe,* by H. Kragh (1996).

The field is also remarkable because, in a relatively short time, an entire discipline has been built up based on (a)incoming electromagnetic fields; (b)gravitational observations, especially of the solar system; and (c)the measurements made in physics laboratories here on earth. There are large gaps in knowledge. Some of the cosmological principles are reviewed here, followed by conjecture designed to literally fill in some of the empty spaces.

In the standard cosmological model, all of the matter and energy in the universe came together, in what is called the Big Crunch, to form a relatively tiny sphere at an unbelievably high temperature. At what we call time $t = 0$, the sphere began to expand; the outer surface expanded at close to the speed of light (and still does so). This initial scenario is therefore called the Big Bang.

How tiny was the initial sphere? Here we run into nonsense such as "the entire universe was compressed into a point." [I am too embarrassed for the human intellect to cite the author(s) of this gem; it is much worse than the assertions about instantaneous interphoton communication over vast distances. Besides, it is completely unnecessary because there are no Bell-type experiments that hint at a pinpoint origin.] Let us try to look at this a bit more realistically, as follows:

The universe started out, say, as a spherical soup consisting of baryons. Baryons are mostly protons and neutrons. (Electrons are not baryons, and we can disregard them, in any event, because their mass is negligibly small relative to that of baryons.) Baryons are the ingredients for a Black Hole—a concentration of matter so vast, with a gravitational field so strong, that most photons cannot escape. Remember that photons have an effective mass, given in Chap. 3, as

$$m_{\text{eff}} = \frac{fh}{c^2},$$

where f = frequency,
    h = Planck's constant,
    c = velocity of light.

A Black Hole is invisible because of the gravitational attraction for m_{eff}. The trajectories of its infrared- and higher-frequency photons curve sufficiently so that they fall back into the central mass. (Lower-frequency photons, however, have less mass and can possibly escape.) Why did not the universe "commit suicide" by forming a Black Hole? Because the temperature was so high that the baryons were relatively far apart. If anything, this is an argument against the pinhead (pun intended) idea.

Let me quote some values:

How heavy is a baryon? We can use the mass of a neutron, 1.675×10^{-27} kg.

How heavy is the sun? 1.988×10^{30} kg.

How many "suns" in a galaxy? Peebles (pg. 53) gives, for the "giant elliptical galaxy M87," 3×10^{13} solar masses. (It is better to use a giant value to compensate for unseen dark matter.)

How many galaxies in the universe? Peebles (pg. 123) gives 3×10^8.

Then the number of baryons in the universe is

$$\frac{1.988 \times 10^{30} \times 3 \times 10^{13} \times 3 \times 10^{8}}{1.675 \times 10^{-27}} = 1.069 \times 10^{79}$$

In what follows, the cast of characters includes the nuclei of four atoms:

Hydrogen = 1 proton + 0 neutrons

Deuterium = 1 proton + 1 neutron

Tritium = 1 proton + 2 neutrons

Helium = 2 protons + 2 neutrons.

With a charge of +1 because of its proton, deuterium and tritium are isotopic forms of hydrogen. In addition, we will run into the neutrino, which has zero charge, and the positron, which has a charge of +1. Like the electron, the mass of a neutrino or positron is negligible compared to the mass of a proton or neutron.

Now picture the Big Crunch, with baryons furiously bouncing around at a temperature of 10^{10} kelvins (K). It is difficult for us to appreciate the meaning of a temperature of 10^{10} K. Temperature is correlated with the kinetic energy of motion of particles that have mass. At a given temperature one can calculate the average velocity of an electron and, if given its mass, the average velocity of an atom, or molecule, and so forth. The most convenient example is that of an electron accelerated by an electric field. To convert from energy in joules to temperature in degrees Kelvin, we divide by Boltzmann's constant, $k_B = 1.38066 \times 10^{-23}$ J/K:

$$1 \text{ eV} = 1.60218 \times 10^{-19} \text{ J corresponds to } 11604.5 \text{ K.}$$

For relatively high temperature it is more usual to encounter million electron volt (MeV) units:

$$1 \text{ MeV corresponds to } 1.16045 \times 10^{10} \text{ K.}$$

According to Table 4-1, if 1 MeV (or 10^6 V) is applied to an electron in the equivalent of a cathode-ray tube, it will end up with a velocity of 2.821×10^8 m/s, or 94.11% the velocity of light and, with $\gamma = 2.957$, there are substantial relativistic effects.

A temperature of 10^{12} K corresponds to an electron accelerated through 86.17 MeV. This falls just above the last row in Table 4-1.

At a temperature of 10 million kelvins (10^7 K), for example, baryons rush about at a speed of around 1,300,000 meters/second (1.3×10^6 m/s). A temperature of 10^{10} K is, of course, 1000 times hotter and more energetic than 10^7 K. Later on in this chapter, this is increased by an additional factor of 100, to 10^{12} K. At that temperature, baryons should "rush about" at a speed close to the maximum, the velocity of light, 3×10^8 m/s. We do not know, however, how matter behaves at a temperature of 10^{12} K.

During the Big Crunch, every once in a while, two baryons fuse, generating new particles at an even higher temperature. As luck would have it, however, we are experts in the field of nuclear fusion because it is the process taking place in fusion bombs and, of course, in stars. The first reaction to occur when baryons are brought together is the fusion of deuterium and tritium [S. P. Parker, *Encyclopedia of Physics,* 1993]:

Deuterium + tritium = helium + neutron + 17.6 MeV.

This equation indicates that 17.6 MeV of energy is released if deuterium and tritium nuclei momentarily combine to form helium and a neutron. There is a net loss of mass, which is converted into the equivalent of 17.6 MeV, in accordance with $m = E/c^2$. The 17.6 MeV corresponds to a temperature of 2.042×10^{11} K, which shows up as increased kinetic energy of motion of the end products (in addition to the motion they already have corresponding to, perhaps, 10^{12} K).

The Big Bang's "soup" has to be thick enough for the above D-T reaction to occur often enough to initiate a chain reaction. How thick? As the deuterium and tritium nuclei fly about, the effective collisional area, or cross section, has to be 5×10^{-28} meter squared. This approximately corresponds to a cube in which each edge is 2.5×10^{-14} meter (or 0.000 25 Å) long. I conjecture that the Big Crunch ended when the average density of the baryon soup was such that each of them occupied, in effect, a volume equal to this 2.5×10^{-14} meter cube.

According to this, multiplying the cube's volume by the number of baryons, we get the volume of the infant universe as

$$(2.5 \times 10^{-14})^3 (1.069 \times 10^{79}) = 1.670 \times 10^{38} \text{ cubic meters.}$$

Assuming that the shape was spherical, and remembering that the volume of a sphere is $4\pi r^3/3$, the Big Bang started out as a sphere with a radius of

$$\left(\frac{1.670 \times 10^{38} \times 3}{4\pi} \right)^{1/3} = 3.416 \times 10^{12} \text{ meters,}$$

or the diameter was 6.833×10^{12} m. Since the distance to the sun is 1.496×10^{11} m, the radius of the Big Bang was only 23 times that of the earth's orbit. We can almost visualize the grand event as it took place. Let not familiarity, however, breed contempt!

The violent, chaotic motion, at a temperature of 10^{12} K, had to resist gravitational collapse. Is an equivalent 0.000 25 Å cube reasonable? It is around 20 times as large as the diameter of a baryon, which is comparable to the range of the strong force (0.000 014 Å).

8-2. The First Few Minutes

Although the mental image of a 6.833×10^{12} m diameter sphere at 10^{12} K, with baryons jostling each other as if in a 0.000 25 Å average cube, is exciting, to say the least, it is of little concern to cosmologists. They are more interested in temperature versus time. The expansion that began with the Big Bang, at $t = 0$, was accompanied by a rapid decrease in temperature. Figure 8-1 shows temperature T as a function of t, based on data given on page 185 of Peebles. Notice that this is a log-log plot, with temperature given in units of 10^{10} K. As we go back in time, toward $t = 0$, the temperature approaches infinity. Cosmologists simply say, of this conclusion, that "new," unknown physics had to exist. As to what happened at $t < 0$, a frequent response is that it was the termination of the Big Crunch, during which the universe collapsed to a pinhead (or 6.833×10^{12} m sphere, in my depiction) after, say, $t = 34$ billion years. (This figure comes from a model, presented in Section 8-8, in which part of the universe expands for 17 billion years, followed by collapse during the next 17 billion years.)

In considering the birth pangs of the universe, it is convenient to look at three significant instances of time—at $t = 0.1, 0.9,$ and 140 seconds:

At $t = 0.1$ s, $k_B T = 3$ MeV, $T = 3.5 \times 10^{10}$ K: At this temperature, atomic nuclei are disrupted, so that we have free neutrons and protons. Temporary alliances, however, are made and broken, such as

    (a)   electron + proton $\longleftrightarrow$ neutron + neutrino
    (b)   neutrino + proton $\longleftrightarrow$ neutron + positron
    (c)   neutron $\longleftrightarrow$ proton + electron + neutrino
    (d)   neutron + proton $\longleftrightarrow$ deuterium + gamma photon

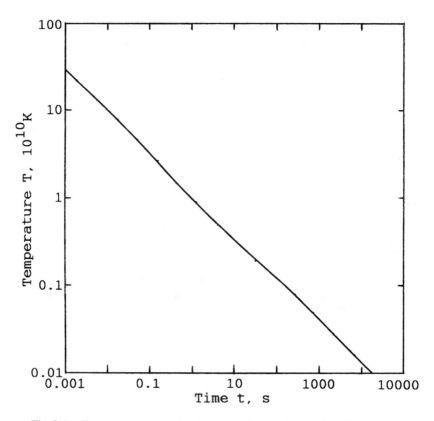

Fig. 8-1.   Temperature versus time during the first few hours of the Big Bang.

In these reactions, charge is conserved, and mass is approximately conserved (minor changes occur because of $E = mc^2$). For reactions that proceed to the right in the above set: In (a), excess energy is carried away by a chargeless neutrino. In (b), positive charge is carried off by the positron. In (d), deuterium consists of a neutron and proton (only the nucleus is involved), and excess energy is carried away by the gamma ray. As indicated, all of the reactions can go to the left as well as right.

In this chaotic exchange that includes neutrons and protons, the neutron/proton ratio is determined by what is known as the thermal equilibrium Boltzmann ratio,

$$\frac{\text{no. of neutrons}}{\text{no. of protons}} = \exp\left[-\frac{(\text{neutron mass} - \text{proton mass})c^2}{k_B T}\right].$$

Numerical substitution yields

$$\frac{\text{no. of neutrons}}{\text{no. of protons}} =$$

$$\exp\left[-\frac{(1.67493 - 1.67262) \times 10^{-27}(2.9979 \times 10^8)^2}{3 \times 10^6 \times 1.6022 \times 10^{-19}}\right] \cong 0.65.$$

[As the temperature decreased, the ratio also decreased. Eventually, at $t \cong 2$ s, the neutron/proton ratio stabilized at one neutron for every seven protons. Working backwards, if we substitute 1/7 for no. of neutrons/no. of protons in the above equations, we get $k_B T = 0.67$ MeV, or $T = 0.77 \times 10^{10}$ K as the effective temperature at which the number of neutrons and protons stabilized.]

At $t = 0.9$ s, $k_B T = 1$ MeV, $T = 1.16 \times 10^{10}$ K: At this temperature, 2 neutrons can combine with 2 protons to form helium. A relatively small number of light elements are also generated (deuterium, with 1 proton and 1 neutron; helium "3," with 2 protons and 1 neutron; lithium, with 3 protons and 4 neutrons; and so forth). One of the reasons that cosmologists are enthusiastic about the Big Bang scenario is that their calculations agree with the amounts of helium and other light elements actually observed after allowing for the fractions lost to nuclear fusion.

At $t = 140$ s, $k_B T = 0.1$ MeV, $T = 0.116 \times 10^{10}$ K: At this temperature, gamma-ray photons lack the energy to direct the last reaction listed under $t = 0.1$ s, (d), from right to left. To disassociate a deuterium nucleus into a neutron and proton, it has to be hit by a photon of energy 2.225 MeV or greater. A photon of energy 2.225 MeV = 3.525×10^{-13} J has a frequency, from $f = E/h$, of 5.320×10^{20} Hz; this is a typical gamma ray. As the last reaction listed under $t = 0.1$ s, (d), goes from left to right, deuterium is formed, but it in turn contributes to the formation of helium by way of the following:

(a) deuterium + deuterium $\longleftrightarrow$ tritium + proton

(b) deuterium + deuterium $\longleftrightarrow$ helium "3" + neutron

(c) tritium + deuterium $\longleftrightarrow$ helium + neutron

(d) helium "3" + deuterium $\longleftrightarrow$ helium + proton

The number of protons (P) and neutrons (N) on the left have to equal the number of Ps and Ns on the right. The following tabulation is a check on this balance:

	P N	P N	P N	P N
(a)	1 1	+ 1 1	= 1 2	+ 1 0
(b)	1 1	+ 1 1	= 2 1	+ 0 1
(c)	1 2	+ 1 1	= 2 2	+ 0 1
(d)	2 1	+ 1 1	= 2 2	+ 1 0

The main significance of the above set of equations is that it accounts for the production of helium.

8-3. Formation of Structures

As the universe expands, various structures form, depending on the local velocity of expansion. The reason for this is that the expansion velocity is tied in with the baryon temperature and density. For example, although the reactions listed under $t = 140$ s do not specify the baryon density, they imply that, at $t = 140$ s, the temperature (1.16 billion K) and density were appropriate for the formation of helium nuclei.

To an astronomer on earth, the most convenient indicator of expansion velocity is the Doppler shift parameter z, which was introduced in Chap. 7:

$$z = \frac{f_{actual}}{f_{observed}} - 1.$$

Locally, if $f_{actual} = f_{observed}$, then $z = 0$. According to Peebles (pgs. 361 and 548), we can now see as far as the distance corresponding to $z = 5$ (but the vision is extremely dim, of course). Visual resolution has considerably improved with the aid of the Hubble satellite telescope. At $z = 5$, the redshift factor, $f_{actual}/f_{observed}$, is 6. An object that would be seen locally as green ($f = 5.7 \times 10^{14}$ Hz) is Doppler shifted down into the infrared at $f = 0.95 \times 10^{14}$ Hz. An object that would be "seen" locally as ultraviolet at $f = 34.2 \times 10^{14}$ Hz is Doppler shifted down to green at $f = 5.7 \times 10^{14}$ Hz, and so forth.

In a collaboration with Craig Hogan, Peebles gives an interesting "timetable" for the formation of structures and processes, versus z values, on page 611. The Peebles–Hogan listing forms the basis for Table 8-1, which is augmented by "t" and "How long ago?" columns, as explained later.

Table 8-1   Timetable for the formation of structures and processes.

Structure or Process	Approximate z	Time t, Years	How Long Ago?, Yrs.
Big Bang	∞	0	1.7×10^{10}
Gravitational potential fluctuations	> 1000	5.4×10^{5}	1.7×10^{10}
Spheroids of galaxies	20	1.8×10^{8}	1.7×10^{10}
The first engines for active galactic nuclei	> 10	4.7×10^{8}	1.7×10^{10}
The intergalactic medium	10	4.7×10^{8}	1.7×10^{10}
Dark matter	> 5	1.2×10^{9}	1.6×10^{10}
Dark halos of galaxies	5	1.2×10^{9}	1.6×10^{10}
Angular momentum of rotation of galaxies	5	1.2×10^{9}	1.6×10^{10}
First 10% of the heavy elements	> 3	2.1×10^{9}	1.5×10^{10}
Cosmic magnetic fields	> 3	2.1×10^{9}	1.5×10^{10}
Rich clusters of galaxies	2	3.3×10^{9}	1.4×10^{10}
Thin disks of spiral galaxies	1	6.1×10^{9}	1.1×10^{10}
Superclusters, walls, and voids	1	6.1×10^{9}	1.1×10^{10}
At the present time	0	1.7×10^{10}	0

The Peebles–Hogan timetable in Table 8-1 is presented with a minimum of comment because the latter is the province of a book on cosmology. It is exciting, however, to think that we can see, past the formation of rich clusters of galaxies at $z = 2$ (14 billion years ago), to $z = 5$ (16 billion years ago). Unfortunately, because they are invisible, one can only infer the formation of dark matter and the dark halos of galaxies.

8-4. Galactic Recession

Every once in a while somebody tells me that the notion that the universe is expanding is all wrong because we seem to be in the center of the universe, and the likelihood that the Big Bang occurred here, in the solar system, is close to zero. This viewpoint is a tremendous improvement over the Ptolemaic system of the second century A.D., in which the earth *was* the center of the universe, with the moon, planets, and stars revolving around the earth. The correct heliocentric planetary motion was not enunciated until Nicolaus Copernicus, around 1500.

With regard to where the Big Bang took place, nature is again responsible for a grand illusion: Yes, the Big Bang probably did not occur in the solar system but, alas, it is perfectly correct that it should *appear* as if the distant galaxies are receding from us, as if we *are* in the center of the universe! In other words, to a first approximation, it is impossible for us to deduce where the Big Bang occurred.

This is illustrated in the two-dimensional cross section of the universe in Fig. 8-2(a). B is the location of the Big Bang, the true center of the universe. Recession of the galaxies from B is indicated by a line drawn through each galaxy. These are vectors: the length is proportional to velocity, which is proportional to distance from B, and the angular orientation represents direction of the expansion. (I tried to add arrows at the end of each line, as is customary for a vector, but this had a confusing side effect, so the lines are shown bare. Besides, arrows are somewhat redundant because all of the lines are headed away from B.)

To avoid distracting complications, it is assumed in what follows that the recession velocity is small compared to the velocity of light.

The earth is represented in the diagram by E. It is convenient to locate E on the zero-degree axis, but there is nothing special about this orientation. (Remember that the earth is also, of course, receding from B.)

A galaxy that is used as an example in what follows is located at point P. It is receding from point B with velocity

$$v_B = H_0 r,$$

where r is the distance from B to P, and H_0 is the Hubble constant [Edwin P. Hubble (1889–1953)] (the numerical value is given below).

Velocities are broken up into horizontal (H) and vertical (V) vector components. In Fig. 8-2(b),

velocity of P relative to B $\begin{cases} \text{H comp} = H_0 r \cos\theta \\ \text{V comp} = H_0 r \sin\theta \end{cases}$

and it turns out that, in Fig. 8-2(c),

velocity of P relative to E $\begin{cases} \text{H comp} = H_0 \rho \cos\phi \\ \text{V comp} = H_0 \rho \sin\phi \end{cases}$

In other words, the velocity of galaxy P relative to E (earth) is only a function of distance to the earth (ρ) and direction to the earth (ϕ). The velocity is completely independent of distance to the Big Bang (r) and direction to the Big Bang (θ). An astronomer on earth, looking at P, can only measure ρ and ϕ, and remains completely ignorant about the "center of the universe."

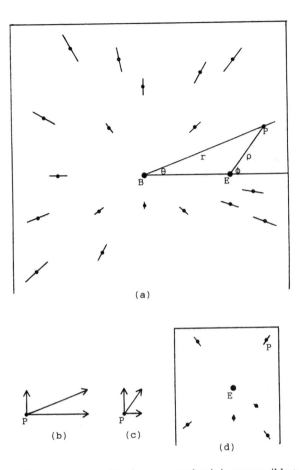

Fig. 8-2. Construction used to demonstrate that it is not possible to determine the location of the Big Bang relative to the earth: (a)Two-di-
mensional depiction of a simplified "universe." The Big Bang
occurred at B, the earth is at E, and a galaxy that is used as an example is located at P. All galactic objects are receding from B with
velocity proportional to distance from B. The lines through each
object are vectors representing recession velocity and direction,
but vector arrows are omitted for the sake of clarity. (b)Vector
components of the recession of P from B. (c)Vector components of
the recession of P from E. (d)The universe as seen from E, including the six nearest galaxies. Although they are actually receding
from B, this information is hidden because they actually appear to
be receding from E.

According to the above, galaxy P is receding from the earth E with velocity $H_0 \rho$. This is depicted in Fig. 8-2(d). Also shown are five other galaxies that are relatively near the earth in (a). In each case, the velocity vector in (d) has been drawn, to scale, to represent velocity relative to E. This is what our earth-bound astronomer sees.

Anywhere in the universe, an observer astronomer sees the galaxies receding from him or her even though, in reality, they are receding from the Big Bang at B. The location of B remains hidden by the simple trigonometric equations given above. Notice that H_0 is a truly universal constant because it is the same for P whether receding from B or from E. Therefore, if we ever succeed in communicating with a distant observer, we will at least be able to agree on H_0 after defining our time unit, the second.

All of the above has little to do with quantum mechanics, but it literally stretches the ether. If the latter does exist, it has to recede along with the galaxies that are embedded in it. This is not a problem if, as conjectured, the ether is a perfectly elastic and lossless medium; that is, if its expansion does not interact via force or energy with the minuscule wave packets that we call photons and electrons.

8-5. The Hubble Constant

What is the value of H_0? Because the measurement entails many uncertainties, the value keeps changing as measurements become more accurate, but there is nothing that one can call an "official" value. This is an unsatisfactory situation for somebody who is writing a paper or book. Even with modern word processors, it can become nerve-racking, and lead to numerical errors, if one has to revise H_0 every few months. Therefore, since this book is full of conjectures anyway, I seized upon one particular value and have ignored the constant stream of individually voiced or published revisions since then. I have cast my lot with Allan Sandage (*New York Times*, 5 March 1996): $H_0 = 57$ km/s per megaparsec.

This is in a form convenient for cosmologists but, in basic meter-kilogram-second units, H_0 is a per-second value, as follows:

$$1 \text{ megaparsec} = 3.262 \times 10^6 \text{ light-years};$$

$$1 \text{ light-year} = 9.4605 \times 10^{15} \text{ meters};$$

$$1 \text{ megaparsec} = 3.086 \times 10^{22} \text{ meters},$$

so that

$$H_0 = \frac{57\ 000\ \text{m/s}}{3.086 \times 10^{22}\ \text{m}} = 1.847 \times 10^{-18}\ \text{per second.}$$

Exactly what does this mean? Is it the rate at which you and the world about you (if not your ego) are expanding per second? Yes, in a way. It is the *average* rate at which disconnected objects, such as individual stars, are expanding (receding from each other). It is a very small number, as is brought out in the answer to the following question: How far away are stars that are receding at a velocity of 1 meter/second from the earth? They are at

$$\frac{1}{1.847 \times 10^{-18}}\text{m} = 5.414 \times 10^{17}\ \text{m} = 57.23\ \text{light-years.}$$

Continuing with these very informative calculations: If 57.23 light-years corresponds to 1 m/s, how far away from us are galaxies that are receding at the velocity of light?

$$57.23 \times 2.998 \times 10^8 = 17.16\ \text{billion light-years.}$$

This fits in nicely with Sandage's report that the universe is at least 15 billion years old. It fits in with a Big Bang whose outer-shell components flew off at close to the speed of light. Components inside the sphere, which had a radius of 3.416×10^{12} m (according to calculations in Section 8-1), flew away from the center with velocity proportional to distance from the center.

The Hubble "constant" is a function of time. It gets smaller as the universe ages. (The change in one of *our* lifetimes is negligible.)

8-6. Some Galactic Peculiarities

Returning to Table 8-1: Now that we have a value for the age of the universe, we can tie this in with the z values. Peebles, on page 102, gives t proportional to $1/(1 + z)^{1.5}$. Our local vicinity, where $z = 0$, has been in existence for 17.16 billion years, so

$$t = \frac{1.716 \times 10^{10}}{(1 + z)^{1.5}}\ \text{years.}$$

This supplies the values in the t column of Table 8-1. The "How long ago?" column is equal to $1.716 \times 10^{10} - t$. For example: The first 10% of the heavy elements formed 2.1 billion years after the Big Bang, or 15 billion years ago. Thin disks of spiral galaxies started to form 6.1 billion years after the Big Bang, or 11 billion years ago, and so forth.

But wait a moment (or would a light-year be more appropriate?)!: Suppose that precursors of our solar system were near the outer shell when the Big Bang occurred. Looking back, we on earth would see the galaxies receding from us with $H_0 = 1.847 \times 10^{-18}$ per second. But looking forward, we would see nothing, only a dark void without stars. Since, on the contrary, the universe appears to be approximately uniform, the earth seems to be, after all, relatively near the center of the universe, at the BBB (Big Bang's Birthplace)!

There are other disquieting phenomena. Heinrich W. M. Olbers (1758–1840) pointed out that the night sky of an infinite, homogeneous universe should be bright, no different from the daylight sky. This notion is called Olbers's paradox. Wherever we look, the integrated effect of distant, and yet more distant, stars and galaxies should yield nothing less than a bright, sunlit sky everywhere. Unless, of course, if distant light is absorbed on the way to our night sky. Some of this certainly occurs, since dark clouds of cosmic "dust" obscure many regions of the Milky Way. Nevertheless, to a first approximation, it *appears* as if the universe is finite, with the earth at the center, because the night sky is uniformly dark.

Furthermore, there is the cosmic background radiation (CBR). It is the cooled-down remnant of the Big Bang. The latter, at $t \cong 1$ second, had a temperature of 10^{10} K; that is, electrons, protons, and neutrons were in chaotic interaction with a kinetic energy corresponding to 10^{10} K. As the universe expanded, the elementary particles, including atoms and molecules, cooled off until, today, their kinetic energy corresponds to blackbody radiation of 2.726 K. The universe is bathed by "light" at this temperature; it is detected as a background noise level. For a long time, radio astronomers marveled at how uniform the CBR happened to be (again, as if the earth was the center of a finite universe). More recently, however, much is made of apparently minute variations in the CBR. After all, the universe had to start with small inhomogeneities that acted as nucleating points for galaxies and stars to form via gravitational attraction.

Finally, some very difficult measurements have shown that the Local Group (group of galaxies relatively close to and including the Milky Way) is moving relative to the CBR. Here is a quote from Peebles, pages 151 and 152:

Blackbody radiation can appear isotropic [invariant with respect to direction] only in one frame of motion. An observer moving relative to this frame finds that the Doppler shift makes the radiation hotter than average in the direction of motion, cooler in the backward direction. That means the CBR acts as an ether, giving a local definition for preferred motion. This does not violate relativity; it always is possible to define motion relative to something, in this case the homogeneous sea of radiation .... The velocity of the Local Group relative to the CBR is 600 km/s. ...

Here a direction is given based on a rectangular-coordinate system: The x axis toward the center of the Milky Way, y axis in the disk in the direction of rotation of the galaxy, and z axis normal to x and y.

In other words, we do not know where the center of the universe is located, but Doppler frequency shifts show that the Local Group, to which we belong, is moving with a certain velocity and direction with respect to the cosmic background radiation. (Incidentally, the Solar System is moving at a velocity of 300 km/s, in a known direction, with respect to the Local Group. Again, distances are so vast that the change in one of *our* lifetimes is negligible.)

After the Big Bang, regions that had slightly higher-than-average concentrations of helium began to coalesce via gravitational attraction. As the atoms fell toward each other, their gravitational potential energy was converted into energy of motion—kinetic energy—in accordance with $mv^2/2$. Higher velocity represented higher temperature, until nuclear fusion could begin. Inside stars, nuclear fusion converts helium and other nuclei into still other nuclei, with a net loss of mass that is converted into energy via $E = mc^2$.

8-7. Entropy

How will it all end? Entropy is a measure of the randomness, disorder, or chaos in the system. A familiar refrain is that "the entropy of the universe is increasing"; that is, much of the mass, and nonthermal forms of energy, are degenerating into heat. This is hardly the place to go into the many cosmological details, which greatly depend on the size of the galactic object, but we eventually get cold, dark matter. What happened to all of the energy that was converted into heat? In accordance with Olbers's paradox, the heat

energy becomes a CBR that simply radiates outward, away from the putative Big-Bang center, as the universe continues to expand and cool off. Not
a very exciting ending, and considerably less dramatic than the end of the
earth, which is scheduled to occur in 5 billion years, when the sun becomes
unstable.

It is a common misconception that entropy always has to increase. It
has to increase for the system as a whole, but for some elements in the system, the entropy can decrease. A living body, taking in a chaotic assortment
of amino acids, assembles them into organized proteins, and so forth, that
have less entropy than the original raw materials.

Here is a simple example: The change in entropy, ΔS, is defined as

$$\Delta S = \frac{\Delta Q}{T},$$

where ΔQ = heat energy entering the object
$\quad\quad T$ = temperature.

Suppose, to illustrate, that object 1 is at 400 K and is connected, by means
of a good heat conductor, to object 2, which is at 500 K. It is found that an
exchange rate of 2000 joules per second takes place. (The temperature
change during the second is negligible.) Then

$$\Delta S_1 = \frac{2000}{400} = 5 \text{ J/K per s, and } \Delta S_2 = -\frac{2000}{500} = -4 \text{ J/K per s.}$$

The entropy of the system increases 1 J/K per s. Energy is conserved, but
entropy is *not* conserved. The hotter element cools off; the average velocity of its atoms and molecules decreases; hence, a decrease in entropy. The
system approaches a final equilibrium state in which both elements have
the same temperature and total entropy is maximum.

With the inclusion of adiabatic (zero heat transfer) processes, entropy
calculations can become quite complicated. The main conclusion for us, of
course, is that the entropy of the universe will increase until a final equilibrium state of cold, dark matter, is reached.

8-8. A Re-entrant Steady-State Universe

If we look at the standard cosmological Big Bang model, there are several
disquieting features:

First, the process is discontinuous. Suddenly, at what we call time $= 0$, condensed matter and energy following a Big Crunch, or whatever, started to expand. We immediately run into a major problem: Expansion of the present universe shows no evidence that it will ever end. This "open" universe is a very illogical and unhappy conclusion. Our hope is that gravitational attraction will eventually cause the expansion to slow down and end (a "closed" universe), followed by contraction toward that happy day—the Big Crunch—that will set the stage for a repeat performance of the Big Bang. The amount of matter detected so far is perhaps 20% of what is needed to close the universe. Astronomers, unhappy with an open universe, have been making heroic attempts to search for the missing 80%. As time goes on, alas, the hope of finding it has been fading.

Second, what was the reality at $t < 0$? How can time have a beginning, or end? Some physicists have proposed that time can run backward. All of this is far beyond human experience.

Third, if entropy always increases, even repetitive Big Bang–Big Crunch–Big Bang – ... cycles will not save us. Eventually, the cycles will end; only a single cold clump of matter will remain, held together forever by gravitational attraction. (Of course, billions of years before that, when the sun becomes unstable, all of man's efforts will have come to naught.)

In an effort to salvage something out of the above chaos, much of which is the conjecture of cosmologists, Fig. 8-3 depicts the model of a re-entrant steady-state universe. It is probably as valid as the old anatomical portrayal of the human egg cell as a homunculus waiting to be fed. In the meantime, as we await future discoveries, conjecture is in order.

In Fig. 8-3, space is curved so that, *somehow,* the expansion is reversed after 17 billion years—not by gravitational attraction, but by two funnels formed by the curvature of space, or by the curvature of streamlines in the ether. According to Einstein's general theory of relativity, mass is associated with gravity, which distorts the geometry of space and time, forcing matter to move along curved paths. Here it is conjectured that the funnels finally end in a kind of Big Crunch—but in a spherical soup much smaller than the 6.833×10^{12} meters in diameter derived in Section 8-1. As matter and energy are compressed in the funnels, the temperature rises to 10^{12} K or greater. Just as a living structure represents local organization and decrease in entropy, compression in the funnels bestows greater organization by way of the ethereal streamlines, and this corresponds to decreasing entropy. The idea here is further detailed as follows.

Consider a cubic volume of gas that becomes compressed in the x and y directions so that the molecules are only free to randomly vibrate in the

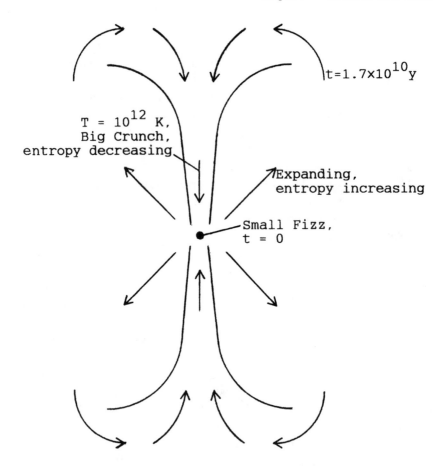

Fig. 8-3. Model of a re-entrant steady-state universe. After 1.7×10^{10} years of expansion, matter returns to the center of the universe, directed by two funnels that are somehow generated by the curvature of space. In the funnels, because of new physics at temperature $\geq 10^{12}$ K, matter is re-created in accordance with $m = E/c^2$. Instead of a Big Bang, we have a Small Fizz. The entire cycle has a period of 3.4×10^{10} years.

z direction. Compression tends to heat the gas (increase its average velocity) but, whereas the expanding universe features mc^2 converted into E via fusion inside stars, in the funnels of Fig. 8-3, at 10^{12} K, new physical principles direct the reversal from E/c^2 into m. Thus, as it is compressed, the temperature of the "gas" does not increase, because energy is converted into mass.

The "Big Bang" is now a misnomer. No longer a 6.833×10^{12} m diameter explosion, I now call the central core a "Small Fizz." The Big Crunch and Small Fizz are two phases—compression and expansion—of a steady-state process.

The Small Fizz sounds like one of those phony nostrums that can cure any human malady. For example: One of the mysteries is how galaxies can form out of the relatively smooth "soup" created by the Big Bang. No problem, of course, for the Small Fizz model. As mass at $T = 10^{12}$ K is created via $m = E/c^2$, it bubbles out of the hopper in the form of huge nonuniform matter blobs that gravitationally condense into elliptical, or spiral (like our own Milky Way), or irregular galaxies.

As we peer at the heavens, is there any evidence that space is extensively curved? Alas this, too, is forever hidden from us. We receive all photons, all rays of light, as if they come to us along straight paths. Perhaps space is curved around the surface of a huge sphere, so we can see "ourselves" as we were 17 billion years ago!

The re-entrant steady-state universe never dies; it is always in transition. But what about time? When did time begin? There is also a conjecture here: The movement of every molecule, atom, electron, proton, neutron, and so forth is governed by four precise laws: gravitation, electromagnetic, strong force, and weak force. When the universe recycles, all of its constituents recycle *exactly,* fully predetermined by the four basic laws, as they did, say, 34 billion years, previously. This deterministic viewpoint is the basis for Chap. 2. Thus time never had a beginning, nor end, but keeps recycling with a period of 34 billion years. The joy in all this is that man comes alive, again, every 34 billion years, but let us temper this joy by subtracting the recurrent horror, the endless litany of man's inhumanity to man.

8-9. The Ether

Except for determinism as discussed in Chap. 2, all of the conjectures in this book seem to have some connection with THE ETHER. Now that we have reached the end of the book, it is appropriate to gather up all of those ethereal conjectures and feed them into this final section as a sort of summary.

The ether was really born in 1864, as a necessary adjunct of Maxwell's equations. An electromagnetic field (EMF) is a propagation of $\underline{E}$ and $\underline{H}$ fields that are at right angles to each other and to the direction of propagation.

Because the fields are transverse, the ether cannot be a liquid or gas, since the latter cannot propagate transverse forces. The ether is therefore a jelly-like or solid medium; furthermore, it has definite properties that are analogous to those of our everyday solids. These are discussed in connection with Table 3-1.

The ether is a perfectly elastic, lossless, linear material. The notion of zero attenuation has become more palatable given the discoveries of superconductivity and superfluidity. A major departure, however, is that the ether does not interact with "our world" where energy is concerned. Since $E = mc^2$, there is also no interaction where mass is concerned. In other words, in all of the instances in this book in which the ether plays a part, there is never an exchange of energy or mass with the ether. Photons and electrons are intimately involved with the ether, but energy or mass never change hands. The ether cannot increase its average velocity, in accordance with the kinetic theory of heat, by locally absorbing energy.

Remember that material objects (an atom's nucleus and its orbiting electrons) occupy a minuscule amount of volume. If one wishes to visualize the ether, it is some kind of "substance," elusive to the human intellect, that fills all of space, interrupted here and there by tiny wave packets and their wave-particle or particle-wave duality fields.

It may be instructive to compare the photon and electron models, Figs. 3-6 and 4-5, respectively: From the two-slit *single-photon* interference pattern experiments of Chap. 3, it is conjectured that each photon consists of a "power pack" that is preceded by a mysterious wave-particle duality (WPD) field. It is conjectured that the latter really consists of (nominally) a compression shock wave that carries zero energy. The photon has been launched with energy $E = fh$. In its power pack, a wave packet resides with frequency $f = E/h$. The wavelength of its wave packet determines the wavelength of its WPD field as it plows through the ether without loss of energy.

From the two-slit *single-electron* interference pattern experiments of Chap. 4 [Tonomura et al., 1989], it is conjectured that each electron consists of a "power pack" that is preceded by a mysterious PWD field. It is conjectured that the latter really consists of (nominally) a compression wind wave that carries zero energy. The power pack is characterized by mass, charge, and spin. Electrons, also, are able to fly through the ether (or a perfect vacuum) without loss of energy.

When electrons fly through the ether, they suffer an increase in effective mass: $m_{eff} = \gamma m_0$.

For the photon, $E = mc^2$ yields $m_{eff} = fh/c^2$ whereas, for the electron, the energy-mass equivalence becomes $E = mv^2$, so $f = E/h = mv^2/h$. However, since the electron's mass has increased by a factor γ, it is more convenient to use $f = \gamma m_0 v^2/h$. Finally, since wavelength $= v/f$, we get an important equation for the PWD wavelength:

$$\lambda_{\text{PWD}} = \frac{h}{\gamma m_0 v}.$$

Is this derivation of λ_{PWD} valid? Using my notation, in the Tonomura et al. report:

"Electrons are emitted from a field-emission tip by an applied electrostatic potential $V_1 = 3$ to 5 kV, and then accelerated to the anode of potential $V = 50$ kV. The electron beam accelerated to V is associated with a wave of wavelength ... which, in the present case, is 0.054 Å."

Notice that, in Table 4-1, if $V = 50{,}000$ volts, then $\lambda_{\text{PWD}} = 0.05355$ Å.

The above λ_{PWD} equation is important because it demonstrates that wavelength is a function of the electron's velocity via two variables in the denominator: γ and v. Velocity with respect to what? It is my conjecture that it is velocity with respect to the ether in which it is embedded. The electron can be inside a cathode-ray tube, or orbiting an atomic nucleus, or wherever.

Perhaps γ is born out of $E = mc^2$ or $E = mv^2$, and has no connection with the ether. But v in the denominator makes sense if the ether has the equivalent of inertia and elasticity, which it seems to have. According to Table 3-1, inertia is represented by $\mu = 1.257 \times 10^{-6}$ henries/meter, and the modulus of elasticity corresponds to $1/\varepsilon = 1.129 \times 10^{11}$ meters/farad. These values yield $c = 2.998 \times 10^8$ meters/second and $Z_0 = 376.7$ ohms.

Returning to the electron model of Fig. 4-5: Perhaps the power pack does not contain a wave packet. Outside, however, the PWD field certainly "knows" that it is flying through the ether, and the compression-expansion lines of Fig. 3-8 squeeze more closely together (λ decreases) as velocity v increases.

The question as to whether the electron's PWD field is transverse or longitudinal remains unsettled, but the waveform of Fig. 4-8 can represent either case.

Turning now to the two-slit single-photon or single-electron interference experiments, the ether enters in three ways:

1. The ether develops streamlines that guide the approaching photon or electron. The power pack and some of its WPD or PWD field enter one slit, while WPD or PWD field (without the power pack) enters the other slit.

2. The WPD or PWD fields interfere constructively and destructively. The ether develops streamlines that guide the power pack toward constructive interference regions.

3. "Guidance" requires the ether to exert lateral forces upon the photon or electron power pack. To do this, the streamlines are characterized as "frictionless guide rails." No energy transfer takes place because the power pack does not change its speed.

Presumably, the lateral push has a negligible effect upon a massive and/or rigid ether.

With regard to a hydrogen atom, the ether enters in two important respects (some of this discussion is pertinent to atoms in general, but only hydrogen is considered in Chap. 5):

First, the orbital frequency is given by

$$f_{\text{orb}} = \frac{m_0 v^2}{nh},$$

where n is the quantum number, a positive integer. The frequency of the electron's PWD field is, with $\gamma = 1$,

$$f_{\text{PWD}} = \frac{m_0 v^2}{h}.$$

Therefore, comparing these frequencies, in a stable orbit, n standing waves are set up. It is conjectured that the ethereal streamlines support or guide the standing waves; the ether only gives way to relatively slow changes in the orbital locus.

Second, it is also conjectured that the ethereal streamlines surrounding the proton nucleus form spherical shells. When an electron occupies one of the stable orbits, it is held in place by a "frictionless guide rail" that supplies all of the lateral force needed to maintain the electron's orbit. The electron, freed from interacting with the nucleus to supply its own centripetal force, is also thus freed from generating synchrotron radiation. Another equally far-fetched explanation is that the curvature of space is not confined to massive stars and galaxies; if a hydrogen proton captures an electron, in any orbit, space becomes *uncurved* so that the electron *behaves* as if it is in a straight-line trajectory. Synchrotron radiation requires, of course, a charged particle in a curved trajectory.

In the equipment used to demonstrate Bell's theorem, a twin-state photon generator creates two almost-identical photons, A and B. In the first setup, Fig. 6-1, the polarization angles are measured. When calcite filter detectors are set to certain angles, it appears as if A and B generate a much greater number of coincidence counts than expected. It is conjectured that the ethereal streamlines, in the calcite filter, are able to impart small, random rotations to the photons' polarization angle, and this accounts for the discrepancy. The randomness is based on the photons' past history, which is statistically random but predetermined.

In the second setup, that of Fig. 6-4, the photons' path length differences are measured in interferometers. The discrepancy of Fig. 6-1 again surfaces. Here it is conjectured that the ethereal streamlines impart small changes in path length by causing the photons to spiral or wobble or zigzag.

In Chap. 7, the ether can be related to two changes displayed by a relativistic electron:

First, its mass apparently increases. This is illustrated by the model of Fig. 4-5: The power pack is accompanied by a compression wind. As velocity increases, wind "resistance" increases, so speed does not increase without limit. Second, in the Lorentz contraction, the degree of contraction is given by

$$\gamma = \frac{1}{[1 - (v/c)^2]^{1/2}}.$$

(γ is also the increase-in-mass factor of a moving object.) Unlike wind resistance in air, there is no exchange of energy due to ethereal wind resistance either in the increase in effective mass, or in the Lorentz contraction.

To explain the Michelson–Morley results of Chap. 7, we have to assume that every large object carries its own ether as it hurtles through space. This is analogous to the earth holding on to the surrounding air because of its gravitational field, a phenomenon that only becomes appreciable in the vicinity of massive bodies. It is tempting to conjecture that the gravitational field of a massive object attracts the ether in accordance with the latter's "density"; as Table 3-1 shows, this is analogous to the permeability $\mu = 1.257 \times 10^{-6}$ henries/meter. If a material has a high magnetic permeability, so that μ is much higher than 1.257×10^{-6} H/m, the increase is due to atomic structure; the all-pervading ether, marred here and there by an atomic constituent, remains with the basic $\mu = 1.257 \times 10^{-6}$ H/m unchanged.

In the re-entrant model of Fig. 8-3, the ether's curved streamlines offer hope that our universe will go on forever because time, instead of beginning and ending, simply repeats over and over again.

Finally, since it is fashionable for books dealing with quantum reality to have a section on "consciousness," I offer one final conjecture: The ether, which is a mysterious, perfectly elastic and lossless "material," is somehow closely connected to consciousness. Since all conjectures based on familiar concepts, such as neural network functioning and architecture, seem to fall short of reasonable acceptance by people who worry about such matters, perhaps the ether, if we can ever find out all of its specifications, will supply the answers.

It seems to me that the ether acts like a smoothing elixir that is much less weird than some aspects of quantum mechanics.

References

D. Z. Albert, "Bohm's Alternative to Quantum Mechanics," *Sci. Am.,* vol. 270, pp. 58–67, May 1994.

A. Aspect, J. Dalibard, and G. Roger, "Experimental Test of Bell's Inequalities Using Time-Varying Analyzers," *Physical Review Letters,* vol. 49, pp. 1804–1807, 1982.

J. Baggott, *The Meaning of Quantum Theory,* Oxford: Oxford Univ. Press, 1992.

J. S. Bell, "On the Einstein Podolsky Rosen Paradox," *Physics,* vol. 1, pp. 195–200, 1964.

J. S. Bell, *Speakable and Unspeakable in Quantum Mechanics,* Cambridge: Cambridge Univ. Press, 1987.

D. Bohm and B. Hiley, *The Undivided Universe: An Ontological Interpretation of Quantum Mechanics,* London: Routledge, 1993.

R. Y. Chiao, P. G. Kwiat, and A. M. Steinberg, "Faster than Light?," *Sci. Am.,* vol. 269, pp. 52–60, Aug 1993.

J. F. Clauser and A. Shimony, "Bell's Theorem: Experimental Tests and Implications," *Reports on Progress in Physics,* vol. 41, pp. 1881–1927, 1978.

D. Deutsch, *The Fabric of Reality,* New York: Allen Lane/Penguin Press, 1997.

P. H. Eberhard and R. R. Ross, "Quantum Field Theory Cannot Provide Faster-than-Light Communication," *Found. Phys. Lett.,* vol. 2, pp. 127–149, 1989.

H. Everett III, "'Relative State' Formulation of Quantum Mechanics," *Reviews of Modern Physics,* vol. 29, pp. 454–462, 1957.

A. P. French, *Special Relativity,* Wokingham: Van Nostrand Reinhold, 1968.

M. Gardner, "Quantum Weirdness," *Discover,* vol. 3, pp. 68–76, Oct. 1982.

S. W. Hawking and R. Penrose, *The Nature of Space and Time,* Princeton: Princeton Univ. Press, 1996.

N. Herbert, *Quantum Reality,* New York: Anchor Books, 1985.

A. Hermann, *The Genesis of Quantum Theory (1899–1913),* Cambridge: MIT Press, 1971.

J. Horgan, *The End of Science,* Corpus Christi: Helix Books, 1996.

H. Kragh, *Cosmology and Controversy: The Historical Development of Two Theories of the Universe,* Princeton: Princeton Univ. Press, 1996.

P. Kwiat, H. Weinfurter, and A. Zeilinger, "Quantum Seeing in the Dark," *Sci. Am.,* vol. 275, pp. 72–78, Nov. 1996.

S. K. Lamoreaux, "Demonstration of the Casimir Force in the 0.6 to 6 μm Range," *Physical Review Letters,* vol. 78, pp. 5–8, Jan. 1997.

D. Lindley, *Where Does the Weirdness Go?,* New York: Basic Books, 1996.

L. Mandel, "Is a Photon Amplifier Always Polarization Dependent?," *Nature,* vol. 304, p. 188, 1983.

R. Mills, *Space, Time, and Quanta,* New York: W. H. Freeman and Co., 1994.

H. R. Pagels, *The Cosmic Code,* New York: Simon & Schuster, 1982.

S. P. Parker , ed., *Encyclopedia of Physics,* 2nd ed., New York: McGraw-Hill, 1993.

Particle Physics Booklet, American Inst. of Physics, July 1994.

P. J. E. Peebles, *Principles of Physical Cosmology,* Princeton: Princeton Univ. Press, 1993.

S. Rado, "Aethro-Kinematics," 1995, 1240 Daniels Drive, Los Angeles, CA 90035.

W. Rindler, *Introduction to Special Relativity,* Oxford: Oxford Univ. Press, 1982.

Scientific American, "Revolution in Cosmology," vol. 280, pp. 45–69, January 1999.

L. S. Swenson, Jr., *The Ethereal Aether,* Austin: Univ. of Texas Press, 1972.

A. Tonomura, J. Endo, T. Matsuda, T. Kawasaki, and H. Ezawa, "Demonstration of Single-Electron Buildup of an Interference Pattern," *Am. J. Phys.,* vol. 57, pp. 117–120, Feb. 1989.

A. Watson, "Quantum Spookiness Wins, Einstein Loses in Photon Test," *Science,* vol. 277, p. 481, 25 July 1997.

E. T. Whittaker, *A History of the Theories of Aether and Electricity,* New York: Thomas Nelson and Sons, 1951; reprinted by Harper & Brothers, 1960.

Appendix

Equations

(Meter-kilogram-second units are generally used in the equations)

Equations of Chapter 2, Section 2-2

For two spherical objects, the gravitational force of attraction is given by

$$F = \frac{GmM}{r^2}, \tag{2-1}$$

where F = force, newtons,

$\quad G$ = gravitational constant, 6.6726×10^{-11} N · m²/kg²,

$\quad m$ = mass (of the lighter object, say), kilograms,

$\quad M$ = mass (of the other object), kilograms,

$\quad r$ = center-to-center distance, meters.

For the special case in which the heavier mass M is stationary while the lighter mass m rotates around M, the centrifugal force appears as

$$F = \frac{mv^2}{r}, \tag{2-2}$$

where v = velocity, meters/second. Combining Eqs. (2-1) and (2-2),

$$v = \sqrt{\frac{GM}{r}}, \tag{2-3}$$

153

independent of the mass of the lighter object, m. (This is why Saturn's rings are stable despite a wide range of masses. The velocity of an object in the ring depends on its distance from Saturn, and not on its mass.) The kinetic energy of an object is given by

$$K = \frac{mv^2}{2}, \tag{2-4}$$

where $K =$ kinetic energy, joules. Substituting for v from Eq. (2-3),

$$K = \frac{GmM}{2r}. \tag{2-5}$$

As a numerical example, for the earth ($m = 5.974 \times 10^{24}$ kg) rotating around the sun ($M = 1.988 \times 10^{30}$ kg) at a distance $r = 1.496 \times 10^{11}$ m,

$$K = \frac{6.6726 \times 10^{-11} \times 5.974 \times 10^{24} \times 1.988 \times 10^{30}}{2 \times 1.496 \times 10^{11}}$$

$$= 2.649 \times 10^{33} \text{ joules.}$$

For a planet, if we integrate force times distance from the planet's idealized initial position, $r = \infty$, to its present orbital radius, r, we get for the potential energy

$$U = -\frac{GmM}{r}. \tag{2-6}$$

Comparing Eqs. (2-5) and (2-6), it is obvious that the magnitude of the potential energy is twice as large as the kinetic energy, but it is negative because the planet has already done work—half has been converted into kinetic energy, the other half into heat (mostly tidal friction). For the earth, therefore, $U = -2K = -5.297 \times 10^{33}$ joules.

Equations of Chapter 2, Section 2-3

Now consider the hydrogen atom of Fig. 2-1(a). The force of attraction between electron and proton is given by

$$F = \frac{ke^2}{r^2}, \tag{2-7}$$

where $k =$ electrostatic constant, 8.9876×10^9 N · m²/C²,

$e =$ electron charge, 1.60218×10^{-19} coulomb.

[The electron and proton charges are equal except, of course, that the electron is negative (by human definition) and the proton is positive.] Equation

(2-7) assumes that there is a well-defined center-to-center distance, r, between the electron and proton wave packets. The centrifugal force is again given by Eq. (2-2), with electron mass m_0 substituting for m. (The electron is not moving fast enough to warrant the relativistic correction, γm_0.) Combining Eqs. (2-2) and (2-7),

$$v = e\sqrt{\frac{k}{m_0 r}}. \qquad (2\text{-}8)$$

Not surprisingly, the velocity is a function of orbital radius.

The angular momentum is given by

$$\mathcal{L} = m_0 v r, \qquad (2\text{-}9)$$

where $\mathcal{L}$ = angular momentum, joule · seconds. But angular momentum is quantized in accordance with

$$\mathcal{L} = \frac{nh}{2\pi}, \qquad (2\text{-}10)$$

where n = the quantum number (1, 2, 3, . . .),

h = Planck's constant, 6.6261×10^{-34} joule · seconds.

Combining Eqs. (2-9) and (2-10),

$$r = \frac{nh}{2\pi m_0 v}. \qquad (2\text{-}11)$$

Next, eliminating v in Eqs. (2-8) and (2-11), we finally get for the allowed orbital radii

$$r = \frac{1}{km_0}\left(\frac{hn}{2\pi e}\right)^2. \qquad (2\text{-}12)$$

As a numerical illustration, here is the calculation for the radius of the first orbit ($n = 1$):

$$r_1 = \frac{1}{8.9876 \times 10^9 \times 9.1094 \times 10^{-31}}\left(\frac{6.6261 \times 10^{-34}}{2\pi 1.60218 \times 10^{-19}}\right)^2$$

$$= 5.292 \times 10^{-11} \text{m},$$

or 0.5292 angstrom (Å).

What is the orbital frequency of the electron? First recall that

$$v = 2\pi r f \qquad (2\text{-}13)$$

where f = orbital frequency. Next, substitute Eqs. (2-12) and (2-13) into Eq. (2-8) to get

$$f = \frac{m_0}{n^3 h^3}(2\pi k e^2)^2. \qquad (2\text{-}14)$$

This, in turn, allows the kinetic energy to be calculated. Combining Eqs. (2-4), (2-12), (2-13), and (2-14),

$$K = 2m_0 \left(\frac{\pi k e^2}{hn} \right)^2. \tag{2-15}$$

For example, numerical substitution yields the frequency and velocity of the first orbit ($n = 1$):

$$f_1 = \frac{9.1094 \times 10^{-31}}{(6.6261 \times 10^{-34})^3} [2\pi 8.9876 \times 10^9 (1.60218 \times 10^{-19})^2]^2$$

$$= 6.580 \times 10^{15} \, \text{Hz}$$

and

$$v_1 = 2\pi 5.292 \times 10^{-11} \times 6.580 \times 10^{15} = 2.188 \times 10^6 \, \text{m/s}.$$

Now we can substitute into Eq. (2-4) to get the electron's kinetic energy:

$$K_1 = \frac{9.1094 \times 10^{-31} (2.188 \times 10^6)^2}{2} = 2.180 \times 10^{-18} \, \text{joule},$$

and for the potential energy, $U_1 = -2K_1 = -4.360 \times 10^{-18}$ joule.

Figure 2-1(b) also shows the $n = 2$ orbit. There are simple relationships between the orbital values. For radius r, Eq. (2-12) shows that it is proportional to n^2, so that

$$r_2 = 4 \times 0.5292 = 2.117 \, \text{Å}.$$

For frequency f, Eq. (2-14) shows that it is inversely proportional to n^3, so that

$$f_2 = 6.580/8 = 0.8225 \, (\times 10^{15}) \, \text{Hz}.$$

For kinetic energy K, Eq. (2-15) shows that it is inversely proportional to n^2, so that

$$K_2 = 2.180/4 = 0.5450 \, (\times 10^{-18}) \, \text{joule},$$

and potential energy $U_2 = -2K_2 = -1.0899 \times 10^{-18}$ joule.

Equations of Chapter 3, Sections 3-1 and 3-2

Table 3-1 lists "derived values" for velocity of propagation and characteristic impedance. For sound, velocity v_s (m/s) is given by

$$v_s = \sqrt{\frac{Y_0}{\rho_D}}, \tag{3-1}$$

where $Y_0 =$ Young's modulus of elasticity, pascals,

    $\rho_D =$ density, kg/m³.

The characteristic impedance Z_0 (ohm) is given by

$$Z_0 = \sqrt{\rho_D Y_0}. \tag{3-2}$$

The analogous expressions for an electromagnetic field are: For velocity v (m/s),

$$v = \sqrt{\frac{1/\varepsilon}{\mu}} = \frac{1}{\sqrt{\mu\varepsilon}}, \tag{3-3}$$

where $\mu =$ permeability, henry/meter,

    $\varepsilon =$ permittivity, farad/meter.

The characteristic impedance Z_0 (ohm) is given by

$$Z_0 = \sqrt{\frac{\mu}{\varepsilon}}. \tag{3-4}$$

Equations of Chapter 3, Section 3-3

It is a simple matter to describe Fig. 3-3(c) analytically. At its right end, ray (1) contributes

$$E_r = \sin(\omega t + 0.5\theta), \tag{3-5}$$

where $E_r =$ relative electric field intensity,

    $\omega =$ radian frequency of the laser beam,

    $\theta =$ phase difference between rays (1) and (2).

At its right end, ray (2) contributes

$$E_r = \sin(\omega t - 0.5\theta). \tag{3-6}$$

This symmetrical form is also used in the waveforms of Fig. 3-3(b). When the sine functions are expanded, some simplification takes place, and we get for the total E_r

$$E_r = 2\cos(0.5\theta)\sin(\omega t). \tag{3-7}$$

In the (1) + (2) waveform of Fig. 3-3(b), where $\theta = 90°$, we have the peak value $2\cos(0.5\theta) = 1.414$, and $\sin(\omega t)$ is recovered without any phase shift.

We have to find the relationship between θ and the difference in path lengths, $\ell_2 - \ell_1$. From the right triangles formed by a, b, and y of Fig. 3-3(a), we get by inspection

$$\ell_2 - \ell_1 = \sqrt{a^2 + (y + b)^2} - \sqrt{a^2 + (y - b)^2}, \qquad (3\text{-}8)$$

where $b = half$ the slit-to-slit center-to-center distance,

$\quad\ a = $ distance from the slit plate to the photographic film,

$\quad\ y = $ vertical distance variable.

Because b is relatively small, one can easily simplify Eq. (3-8) with the aid of $(1 + \triangle)^{1/2} = 1 + 0.5\triangle$ to get

$$\ell_2 - \ell_1 = \frac{2by}{\sqrt{a^2 + y^2}}. \qquad (3\text{-}9)$$

In addition, we have a simple proportion,

$$\frac{\theta}{2\pi} = \frac{\ell_2 - \ell_1}{\lambda}, \qquad (3\text{-}10)$$

where $\lambda = $ wavelength of the laser EMF. Combining Eqs. (3-7), (3-9), and (3-10),

$$A = 2\cos(0.5\theta) = 2\cos\left(\frac{2\pi by}{\lambda\sqrt{a^2 + y^2}}\right), \qquad (3\text{-}11)$$

where $A = $ amplitude of film exposure sine wave. This becomes negative when 0.5θ lies in the second or third quadrant. This is not a problem, however; since exposure depends upon power rather than amplitude, we have to square the right side of Eq. (3-11), which only yields positive values, and divide by 2 to convert from peak to average to get the *magnitude* of film exposure, M:

$$M = 2\cos^2\left(\frac{2\pi by}{\lambda\sqrt{a^2 + y^2}}\right). \qquad (3\text{-}12)$$

This is plotted as the curve of Fig. 3-3(c).

Equations of Chapter 3, Section 3-8

The spectrum of the Fig. 3-10(a) waveform is found as follows: Given a waveform

$$y(x) = \varepsilon^{-\alpha x}\left(\frac{c - b\alpha}{\beta} \sin \beta x + b \cos \beta x\right), \qquad (3\text{-}13)$$

the Laplace transform spectrum is

$$y(s) = \frac{bs + c}{s^2 + 2s\alpha + \alpha^2 + \beta^2}.$$ (3-14)

For Fig. 3-10(a), where $\alpha = 0.1$, $b = 0$, $c = 2\pi$, and $\beta = 2\pi$, the spectrum appears as

$$y(s) = \frac{2\pi}{s^2 + 0.2s + 39.49}.$$ (3-15)

To get the magnitude of the spectrum, first replace s by $j\omega$, where $\omega = 2\pi f$:

$$y(j\omega) = \frac{2\pi}{-\omega^2 + j0.2\omega + 39.49},$$ (3-16)

which leads to the magnitude, $y(\omega)$:

$$y(\omega) = \frac{2\pi}{\sqrt{(39.49 - \omega^2)^2 + (0.2\omega)^2}}.$$ (3-17)

This is plotted as the curve of Fig. 3-10(b).

Equations of Chapter 4, Section 4-1

In deriving the equations for relativistic changes: Since mass is now a function of γ, we have to go to basic definitions for the kinetic energy, K:

$$dK = F\,dx,$$ (4-1)

where a change in potential energy, $F\,dx$, is converted into a change in kinetic energy, dK. Next, replacing force by mass times acceleration,

$$dK = m\frac{dv}{dt}\,dx,$$ (4-2)

which is equivalent to

$$dK = \frac{dx}{dt}\,m\,dv.$$ (4-3)

But dx/dt is velocity, v, and $m\,dv$ is change in momentum, dp, so the basic form derived here is

$$dK = v\,dp.$$ (4-4)

We will return to Eq. (4-4) later on. In the meantime, a questionable assumption is made, but it is dignified by calling it an "intelligent guess" because it seems to work. We assume that the relativistic increase-in-mass factor, γ, is the same as the Lorentz contraction factor, γ. (Recall that γ is equal to or greater than one.) The advantage of this "intelligent guess" is that it is easy to derive γ versus c from the geometry of the Lorentz contraction.

Turning to Fig. 7-1, we have an L-shaped structure, each leg of length ℓ. As a result of horizontal movement (to the right), at velocity v, the length of the horizontal leg changes to ℓ/γ, but the length of the vertical leg remains unchanged because there is no motion in this direction. As Fig. 7-1 depicts, two light beams are launched at the lower-left corner of the L. The velocity of each beam is c. In the absence of contraction, the total length of the lower beam's path would be longer than that of the upper (53°) beam in Fig. 7-1. Because of contraction, however, the total length of the lower beam's path is exactly equal to that of the upper beam. By how much does the horizontal leg have to contract?

From the geometry of Fig. 7-1, we get

$$\gamma = \frac{c}{\sqrt{c^2 - v^2}}, \tag{4-5}$$

or, solving for v,

$$v = \frac{c\sqrt{\gamma^2 - 1}}{\gamma}. \tag{4-6}$$

Momentum, mass times velocity, now appears as

$$p = \gamma m_0 v = m_0 c \sqrt{\gamma^2 - 1}, \tag{4-7}$$

and, differentiating,

$$dp = \frac{m_0 c \gamma}{\sqrt{\gamma^2 - 1}}\, d\gamma. \tag{4-8}$$

The next step is to substitute Eqs. (4-6) and (4-8) into Eq. (4-4). There results the surprisingly simple relationship

$$dK = m_0 c^2 d\gamma. \tag{4-9}$$

Finally, integrating, with a lower limit $\gamma = 1$,

$$K = m_0 c^2 (\gamma - 1). \tag{4-10}$$

In any device that accelerates electrons, such as a cathode-ray tube, assuming that all of the potential energy eV is converted into kinetic energy K, Eq. (4-10) leads to

$$\gamma = \frac{eV}{m_0 c^2} + 1. \tag{4-11}$$

Alternate forms of particle-wave duality frequency f and wavelength λ, as a function of voltage V, appear as

$$f = \frac{eV}{h}\left(\frac{1 + 2m_0 c^2/eV}{1 + m_0 c^2/eV}\right) \tag{4-12}$$

and

$$\lambda = \frac{ch}{eV\sqrt{1 + 2m_0c^2/eV}}. \tag{4-13}$$

Equations of Chapter 5, Section 5-4

The centripetal force F required to maintain an electron in a circular orbit is given by Eq. (2-7), which is repeated here:

$$F = \frac{ke^2}{r^2}, \tag{5-1}$$

where k = electrostatic constant, $8.9876 \times 10^9 \text{ N} \cdot \text{m}^2/\text{C}^2$,

$\quad e$ = electron charge, 1.60218×10^{-19} coulomb,

$\quad r$ = radius of orbit, meters.

The force acting on an electron that is moving at right angles to a magnetic field is given by

$$F = Bev, \tag{5-2}$$

where B = magnetic flux density, teslas,

$\quad v$ = velocity, meters/second.

Combining Eqs. (2-8), (2-12), (5-1) and (5-2), the flux density required for constant r is given by

$$B = (km_0)^2 \left(\frac{2\pi e}{nh} \right)^3. \tag{5-3}$$

For the $n = 1$ orbit, we get

$$B = (8.9876 \times 10^9 \times 9.1094 \times 10^{-31})^2 \left(\frac{2\pi 1.60218 \times 10^{-19}}{6.6261 \times 10^{-34}} \right)^3$$

$$= 235{,}100 \text{ teslas.}$$

Index

A

Accelerator storage ring, 84
Aether: *see* Ether
Air, 30, 31
Albert, D. Z., 70
Angular momentum, 67, 76, 89, 135, 155

B

Baggott, J., 9, 41
Baryon, 128, 129, 130, 131, 134
Beam splitter, 48, 51, 105
Bell, J. S., 8, 89
Bell's theorem, 89, 95, 98, 148
Big Bang, 13, 127, 130, 131, 135, 136,
    139, 141, 143
Big Crunch, 13, 127, 129, 130, 131, 143
Birefringent, 90
Black-body radiation, 140
Black Hole, 128
Blocking plate, 52, 72
Blue shift, 120, 121
Bohm, D., 5, 47
Bohr, N., 76
Boltzmann constant, 4, 129, 132

Brown, R., 16
Brownian movement, 16

C

Calcite filter, 90, 92, 94, 95, 148
Calcium, 89
Capacitance, 32, 34
Casimir effect, 47
Cathode-ray tube, 56, 57, 60, 129
Centrifugal force, 19, 77, 110, 153, 154
Centripetal force, 84, 86, 161
Characteristic impedance, 30, 31, 35,
    147, 156
Chiao, R. Y., 54, 103
Coincidence counter, 93, 94, 95, 97, 106, 148
Combinations, 25, 27
Consciousness, 14, 150
Copernicus, N., 15, 135
Cosmic background radiation, 140, 141

D

De Broglie, L., 58, 76, 79
Decaying-exponential field, 44, 53, 54,
    68, 72

Determinism, 11, 15
Deuterium, 129, 130, 131, 133
Dielectric constant, 34
Diffraction, 34, 36, 46, 60, 61, 63
Doppler shift, 117, 120, 121, 123, 134, 141
Double-slit: *see* Two-slit interference

E

Earth, 4, 19, 110, 154
Einstein, A., 4, 7, 86, 109
Electric field, 32, 34, 35, 63, 84
Electromagnetic field, 1, 3, 6, 29, 38, 75, 84, 89, 92, 109, 127, 145, 157
    plane wave, 32
Electron, 4, 17, 41, 55, 56, 57, 109, 110, 128, 131, 140, 146, 154
    charge, 67
    effective mass, 57, 58, 146, 149, 159
    spin, 67, 70
    velocity, 83
Electrostatic constant, 4, 21, 154, 161
Energy, 38, 43, 44, 146
Entropy, 141, 142, 143
Ether, 2, 9, 42, 47, 66, 109, 111, 114, 117, 123, 126, 138, 145, 147, 150
    jelly, 83
    shock wave, 42, 43, 83, 98, 107, 146
    wind wave, 66, 68, 70, 78, 83, 146, 149

F

Field emission, 61, 147
FitzGerald, G. F., 111
Fluorescent screen, 56, 60, 61, 65
Free will, 11, 16
Frictionless guide rail, 78, 86, 148
Fusion, 130, 133, 141, 143

G

Galaxy, 128, 135, 136, 139, 140
Gamma ray, 46, 59, 133
Gaussian form, 37, 63, 101
Gravitational constant, 4, 153
Graviton, 4

Gravity, 5, 110, 127, 128, 131, 143, 145, 149, 153
    universal law, 55
Ground state, 76, 79, 84, 89

H

Heat: *see* Temperature
Heisenberg, W., 11
Heliocentric model, 15
Helium, 43, 129, 130, 133, 141
Herbert, N. 8, 12
Hogan, C., 134
Horgan, J., 9
Hubble, E. P., 136
Hubble:
    constant, 4, 136, 138, 139
    telescope, 134
Hydrogen atom, 12, 20, 44, 75, 84, 86, 89, 129, 148, 154
    electron orbit frequency, 78, 155
    electron orbit radius, 76, 77, 80
    nucleus, 75, 84, 88

I

Increase-in-mass factor, 57, 59, 68, 112, 114, 149
Inductance, 32, 34
Infrared, 84, 103, 128, 134
Inertial reference frame, 110
Interference, 36, 38, 41, 42, 51, 60, 61, 64, 70, 72, 105, 147
Interferometer, 48, 103, 105, 149
Isolated-electron pattern, 64, 68, 146, 147
Isolated-photon pattern, 40, 44, 92, 98, 106, 146, 147

J

Joint probability, 102, 103

K

Kinetic energy, 19, 21, 47, 57, 59, 60, 67, 78, 84, 86, 129, 130, 140, 141, 153, 155, 159

Kinetic theory of heat, 16, 146
Kwiat, P., 48

L

Laplace transform, 158
Laser beam, 22, 35, 36, 105
Lateral force, 46, 47, 70, 72, 88, 148
Length constant, 53
Lindley, D., 9, 41
Local group, 140, 141
Longitudinal vibration, 30, 44, 48, 68,
    80, 147
Lorentz, H. A., 111
Lorentz contraction, 111, 114, 149, 159
    factor, 112, 114, 117, 121
Lyman series, 22

M

Magnetic field, 32, 34, 35, 83, 84
    flux density, 84, 161
Maxwell, J. C., 1
Maxwell's equations, 1, 6, 7, 84, 145
Mica, 30, 34
Michelson, A. A., 110
Michelson–Morley experiment, 110, 149
Mills, R., 41, 117
Modulus of elasticity, 30, 31, 34, 147, 156
Momentum, 11, 56, 76, 159, 160
Moon, 20, 110
Morley, E. W., 110

N

Neon, 87
Neutrino, 131
Neutron, 17, 22, 24, 26, 55, 109, 110, 128,
    130, 131, 133, 140
Newton, I., 2, 5
Nickel, 30, 31, 60
Nonlocal: see Superluminal
Nucleon, 22, 28

O

Olbers, H. W. M., 140
Olbers's paradox, 140, 141

P

Parsec, 4
Particle-wave duality, 12, 41, 58, 60, 61,
    64, 66, 68, 76, 78, 146, 147
    frequency, 58, 59, 60, 66, 67, 79
    wavelength, 80
Pauli, W., 87
Pauli exclusion principle, 87
Peebles, P. J. E., 127, 140
Permeability, 4, 30, 34, 147, 149, 157
Permittivity, 4, 30, 34, 157
Photomultiplier, 93, 106
Photon, 2, 10, 21, 22, 35, 38, 41, 44, 60,
    61, 78, 109, 128, 131, 133, 146, 148
    detector, 51, 53
    effective mass, 46, 56
    effective momentum, 56
    energy, 103
    model, 29
    reflection, 31
Piezoelectric transducer, 105
Planck, M., 21
Planck:
    constant, 4, 29, 46, 76, 155
    law, 21, 29, 35, 46
Planetary motion, 19
Point particle, 41, 65
Polarization, 34, 35, 44, 68, 89, 90, 92, 94,
    98, 101, 148
    random, 148
    rotation, 98, 100
Positron, 131
Potential energy, 19, 21, 57, 59, 78, 154, 156
Proton, 17, 22, 24, 27, 55, 109, 110, 128,
    131, 133, 140, 154

Q

Quality factor, 53, 74
Quantum mechanics, 2, 7, 41, 70, 75, 76,
    87, 89, 95
Quantum:
    jump, 22, 44, 46, 78, 83
    number, 20, 76, 148, 155
    spiral, 78, 80, 83
Quasar, 109, 110, 117, 120, 123, 126

R

Radioactive decay, 22
Rado, S., 11
Random perturbation, 98, 107
Red shift, 117, 120
    z, 120, 121, 134
Reflection, 42, 70, 79
Refraction, 42, 90
Relativistic effect, 55, 57, 68, 76, 117, 120,
    123, 129, 149, 154, 159
Relativity, 4, 13, 86, 141, 143
Resonant chamber, 79

S

Sandage, A., 138
Saturn, 153
Schrodinger, E., 7
Schrodinger's equations, 16, 20, 22,
    75, 83
Simultaneous-burst pattern, 39, 64
Skeptical Inquirer, 13, 115
Small Fizz, 13, 145
Snell's law, 90
Sound wave, 2, 42, 80, 118, 156
    reflection, 31
Space curvature, 86, 88, 111, 115, 126,
    143, 145, 148, 149
Space vehicle, 115, 116
Spatial:
    frequency, 53, 74
    waveform, 53, 118
Special relativity, 109, 111
Spectrum, 53, 158
Spontaneous fission, 23, 24, 28
Standing wave, 12, 79, 83, 148
Straight-line trajectory, 86, 87, 88, 148
Stream line, 47, 48, 52, 70, 72, 78, 86, 98,
    107, 147, 148
Strong force, 4, 23, 131, 145
    sphere of influence, 24, 27
Sun, 4, 19, 110, 128, 154
Superconductivity, 43
Superfluidity, 43

Superluminal, 8, 89, 95, 97, 105
Synchrotron radiation, 13, 83, 84, 86, 148

T

Temperature, 16, 24, 43, 129, 130, 131,
    133, 140, 141, 143
Time dilation, 115, 117, 120, 121, 126
Tonomura, A., 12, 55, 61, 64, 146, 147
Transverse vibration, 30, 43, 44, 68, 80,
    147
Traveling wave, 79
Tritium, 129, 130, 133
Twin-state photon generator, 89, 103, 148
Two-slit interference, 12, 35, 44, 51, 58,
    60, 61, 64, 68, 147

U

Ultraviolet, 37, 59, 78, 103, 134
Uncertainty principle, 11, 16, 17
Universe, 127, 128, 130
    expanding, 10, 135, 138
    steady-state, 142, 143, 145
Uranium nucleus, 22, 24, 26

V

Vacuum, 1
Velocity of propagation:
    photon, 30, 35, 43, 44, 54, 66, 67, 109,
        110, 117, 121, 147, 156
    sound, 42, 118, 121, 123, 156
Vibrating string, 79
Visible light, 37

W

Water molecule, 20, 30, 31, 34
Waveguide, 32, 35, 79, 98
Wavelength, 146
Wave packet, 41, 56, 109, 126, 146
Wave-particle duality, 8, 41, 43, 51, 52, 58,
    83, 106, 146, 147

X

X ray, 41, 46, 59, 60, 84

Y

Young's modulus: *see* Modulus of elasticity

Z

Zero energy, 43, 47, 52, 60, 66, 67, 72, 78, 146

About the Author

Sid Deutsch was born on 19 September 1918. All of his schooling was in New York City: Stuyvesant High School (Physics prize) in 1935; Cooper Union, B.E.E. in 1941; Polytechnic Institute of Brooklyn (now Polytechnic University), Ph.D. in 1955. He authored or co-authored five technical books. He was associated with the E.E. department of Polytechnic Inst. of Brooklyn (1951–1972); E.E. department of Rutgers Univ. (1972–1979); B.M.E. program of Tel-Aviv Univ. (1979–1983); E.E. department of Univ. of South Florida, Tampa (1983–1998). He is a Fellow of the Institute of Electrical and Electronics Engineers and of the Society for Information Display. He "retired" in September 1998.